DATA
PROCESSING
FOR
BUSINESS

STUDY GUIDE TO ACCOMPANY

DATA PROCESSING FOR BUSINESS

GERALD A. SILVER
LOS ANGELES CITY COLLEGE

JOAN B. SILVER

HARCOURT BRACE JOVANOVICH, INC.
NEW YORK   CHICAGO   SAN FRANCISCO   ATLANTA

N.A.

ISBN: 0-15-516806-1

Library of Congress Catalog Card Number: 72-90642

Printed in the United States of America

To The Student

The Study Guide is designed to help you check your progress in understanding the fundamental concepts explored in *Data Processing for Business.*

Each unit begins with a vocabulary drill containing key terms introduced in the chapter. You should understand the terms well enough to be able to define them in your own words.

Next, self-tests help you evaluate your comprehension of the key concepts presented in the chapter. True or false statements check your knowledge of the various areas covered. Matching statements test your ability to pair key terms and their definitions. Finally, multiple choice statements test your skill in isolating key concepts from closely related or similar topics.

The answers to the true-false, matching statements, and multiple choice statements are included at the end of each unit. Compare your results with those answers before proceeding. If a concept is not clear, reread the related portions in the textbook, or discuss the topic with your instructor.

Several essay questions complete each unit. They are designed to guide you in expressing important concepts in a clear, concise way. The formulation of essay answers will help you clarify details and relationships and point out gaps in your knowledge.

Proper use of the Study Guide will enable you to check your awareness and comprehension of essential concepts and terminology before you move on to the next unit.

Gerald A. Silver
Joan B. Silver

Contents

DATA
PROCESSING
FOR
BUSINESS

Data Processing

VOCABULARY Briefly define the following terms.

1. Data

2. Data processing

3. Data cycle

4. Input

5. Source document

6. Output

7. Program

8. Computer

9. External data flow

10. Internal data flow

SELF-TESTS

TRUE AND FALSE STATEMENTS

T F   1. Computers are general-purpose tools and can solve a variety of problems.

T F   2. Input involves reporting the results in a form comprehensible to man.

T F   3. Data processing involves changing data in form, order, and structure to increase its value.

T F   4. Computers can print out only alphabetic and numeric data.

T F   5. Computers may be classified as either digital or logarithmic.

T F   6. Computer programs are fed into the computer and stored before data is fed in.

T F   7. Self-directing means the operator controls each step as the machine carries out the problem.

T F   8. A report on employee witholdings to government is an example of external data flow.

T F   9. The process of converting source documents into original records is called data input.

T F   10. There is a general tendency toward processing fewer transactions in business.

T F   11. Computers can forecast sales and prepare payrolls, but they cannot provide management reports or schedule work.

T F   12. Processing of airline ticket reservations is an application of data processing.

T F   13. The error level in computers is about one error per 10 million calculations.

T F   14. In banking, a computer can process deposits, loans, and revolving charge accounts.

T F   15. The stored program greatly increases the general-purpose nature of the computer.

T F   16. General ledgers can be stored electronically in computers.

T F   17. Computers are widely used by firms employing more than ten employees.

T F   18. With the advent of computers, there is less need for complete information in the decision-making process.

T F   19. Digital computers process data in the form of numbers or letters.

T F   20. Data rarely flows between the business enterprise and vendors.

MATCHING STATEMENTS Select the matching description for each term from the list on the right.

_____	1.	Input	a.	Unit of larger system
_____	2.	Processing	b.	Original record
_____	3.	Output	c.	Changed in form, order, or structure
_____	4.	Digital computer	d.	Converting data from source document
_____	5.	Business system	e.	Within an organization
_____	6.	Subsystem	f.	Processing numbers or letters
_____	7.	Data	g.	Useful knowledge
_____	8.	Internal data flow	h.	Outside an organization
_____	9.	Source document	i.	Group of related parts
_____	10.	External data flow	j.	Reporting of results

MULTIPLE CHOICE STATEMENTS Circle the correct answer or answers for each statement.

1. Which of the following are examples of data?
   a. personnel
   b. reports
   c. figures
   d. documents

2. Business decisions are based upon
   a. quality of data
   b. accuracy of data
   c. availability of data
   d. all of the above

3. Modeling and planning involve
   a. simulating business
   b. mathematical terms
   c. testing the real thing
   d. finding best combination

4. Which of the following are data processing operations?
   a. merging
   b. hiring
   c. sorting
   d. calculating

5. The data cycle includes
   a. input
   b. input, processing, output
   c. input, output
   d. processing, output

3

6. Which of the following are computers?
   a. abacus
   b. adding machine
   c. slide rule
   d. typewriter

7. Computers can print out
   a. whole paragraphs
   b. plot curves
   c. write letters
   d. all of the above

8. Analog computers can receive data as
   a. pressure
   b. temperature
   c. time
   d. all of the above

9. Data output involves
   a. reading in cards
   b. reading in forms
   c. reading in tapes
   d. printing out forms

10. One of the following instances does *not* constitute vertical data flow.
    a. foreman to line employee
    b. president to branch manager
    c. supervisor to supervisor
    d. supervisor to president

SHORT ESSAY QUESTIONS

1. What demands on the business enterprise emphasize the need for effective data processing?

2. Describe the steps in the data cycle.

3. Contrast analog computers with digital computers.

4. Discuss internal and external data flow.

5. Discuss five specific uses for computers in business.

6. List and discuss a representative sampling of current business data processing examples.

7. Contrast data input with data output.

8. Why have businesses turned to computers to handle their data processing needs?

ANSWERS TO SELF-TESTS

1.	T	11.	F	1.	d	1.	b, c, d
2.	F	12.	T	2.	c	2.	d
3.	T	13.	T	3.	j	3.	a, b, d
4.	F	14.	T	4.	f	4.	a, c, d
5.	F	15.	T	5.	i	5.	b
6.	T	16.	T	6.	a	6.	a, b, c
7.	F	17.	F	7.	g	7.	d
8.	T	18.	F	8.	e	8.	d
9.	F	19.	T	9.	b	9.	d
10.	F	20.	F	10.	h	10.	c

Trends in Data Processing

VOCABULARY   Briefly define the following terms.

1.   Manual method

2.   Unit record method

3.   First-generation computer

4.   Hardware

5.   Software

6.   Machine language

7.   Magnetic ink character reader

8. Optical character reader

9. Open shop

10. Closed shop

SELF-TESTS

TRUE AND FALSE STATEMENTS

T   F   1. Hardware consists of the machines, devices, and mechanisms used to process data.

T   F   2. Software consists of programmers, supervisors, and computer languages.

T   F   3. The abacus consists of a frame and rods strung with beads.

T   F   4. Herman Hollerith developed an automatic system for weaving patterns into fabric.

T   F   5. Magnetic tape is an example of random access storage.

T   F   6. Manual data processing relies heavily upon data cards.

T   F   7. Manual data processing is limited by the speed of the human hand and eye.

T   F   8. Computer output may be by line printer, cathode ray tube, or audio response unit.

T   F   9. It is often easier to solve a single problem by pencil and paper than by computer.

T   F   10. Teleprocessing allows data to be remotely processed.

T   F   11. Hard-copy terminals display images on cathode ray tubes.

T   F   12. In the open shop, only supervised trained operators are allowed to use the computer.

T   F   13. A problem-oriented language resembles ordinary English more than a machine language does.

T   F   14. Time sharing was developed to replace the human attendant in scheduling work.

T   F   15. Proprietary software requires the lease or sale of computer hardware.

T   F   16. Time sharing firms offer systems design and programming services.

T   F   17. Fourth-generation computers use integrated and monolithic currents.

T   F   18. Computer storage devices include magnetic tape, magnetic disk, and typewriter keyboard.

T   F   19. Third-generation computers introduced microtransistors and optical and magnetic ink character recognition devices.

T   F   20. The unit record method uses adding machines, typewriters, and pencils.

MATCHING STATEMENTS Select the matching description for each term from the list on the right.

_____	1.	Second generation	a.	Mnemonics
_____	2.	Magnetic disk	b.	Transistors
_____	3.	Unit record	c.	Data card
_____	4.	OCR	d.	Magnetic character
_____	5.	MICR	e.	Share the cost
_____	6.	Machine language	f.	Babbage
_____	7.	Assembler language	g.	Storage device
_____	8.	Compiler	h.	Optical character
_____	9.	Time sharing	i.	Translator
_____	10.	Analytical Engine	j.	Early computer language

MULTIPLE CHOICE STATEMENTS Circle the correct answer or answers for each statement.

1. The Analytical Engine
   a. was invented by Babbage
   b. used gears and wheels
   c. was an early attempt at mechanizing data processing
   d. all of the above

2. One of the following is *not* an advantage of manual data processing.
   a. ease of implementation
   b. simplicity
   c. flexibility
   d. standardization

3. Limitations of the unit record method include
   a. bulky to store cards
   b. programming by wiring board
   c. cards are easily damaged and mutilated
   d. all of the above

4. The function of a hard-copy terminal is to
   a. type out reports
   b. display reports on cathode ray tubes
   c. store reports
   d. none of the above

5. The advantages of a closed shop include
   a. work can be grouped and run in batches
   b. poor document security
   c. teleprocessing
   d. greater reliability

6. Machine language is characterized by
   a. fast programming time
   b. widely used programming language
   c. use of zeros and ones
   d. none of the above

7. The function of a compiler is to
   a. write Assembler programs
   b. write operating systems
   c. translate programs
   d. none of the above

8. Operating systems
   a. handle error conditions
   b. schedule work more efficiently
   c. handle interruptions
   d. all of the above

9. Services provided by time-sharing companies include
   a. systems design
   b. programming
   c. computer time
   d. all of the above

10. One of the following is *not* a proprietary program.
    a. file maintenance routine
    b. data center director
    c. report writer
    d. personnel management program

SHORT ESSAY QUESTIONS

1. Contrast software and hardware.

2. Explain the concept of the internally stored program.

3. Summarize the major developments in the four generations of computers.

4. Discuss the contributions of Charles Babbage to computer data processing.

5. Contrast the advantages of manual data processing with those of electronic data processing.

6. Summarize the major types of terminals in use.

7. How do machine language, Assembler language, and problem-oriented languages differ?

8. Briefly trace the major innovations and progress in the development of computer hardware.

9. Briefly trace the major innovations and progress in the development of computer software.

ANSWERS TO SELF-TESTS

1.	T	11.	F	1.	b	1.	d
2.	F	12.	F	2.	g	2.	d
3.	T	13.	T	3.	c	3.	d
4.	F	14.	F	4.	h	4.	a
5.	T	15.	F	5.	d	5.	a
6.	F	16.	T	6.	j	6.	c
7.	T	17.	T	7.	a	7.	c
8.	T	18.	F	8.	i	8.	d
9.	T	19.	T	9.	e	9.	d
10.	T	20.	F	10.	f	10.	b

Unit Record and Input Principles

VOCABULARY Briefly define the following terms.

1. Unit record

2. Column

3. EBCDIC

4. Digit rows

5. Zone rows

6. Field

7. Hollerith code

8. File

9. Master record

10. Verify

SELF-TESTS

TRUE AND FALSE STATEMENTS

T F 1. The EAM cycle consists of input, processing, and tabulation.

T F 2. The unit record system means each punched card contains data on only one item.

T F 3. A punched card with student's name, ID, and test score is an example of a unit record.

T F 4. Mark-sense cards require keypunching.

T F 5. The following terms are synonyms for punched card: tab card, data card, IBM card, unit record.

T F 6. A field is a group of related bits punched in one column.

T F 7. The 9 edge refers to the top edge of the card nearest the 9 row.

T F 8. The column 80 end refers to the right edge of the card nearest column 80.

T F 9. The Hollerith code differs from EBCDIC in the punch combinations for the special characters.

T F 10. A System/3 card stores up to 96 columns of data, whereas the standard card holds 80 columns.

T F 11. A logical record contains data related to a single item.

T F 12. Logical records are not limited in size; physical records are limited by the characteristics of the card.

T F 13. A detail record contains selective data copied from a master record, or original data that will be added to the master record.

T F 14. A master record is the same as a summary record.

T F 15. A fixed-length record stores data of different length depending upon the amount required by each transaction.

T F 16. File maintenance is the process of keeping files current and up-to-date.

T F 17. In a mnemonic code, each item is assigned a number in sequence.

T F 18. In a significant digit code, meaning is assigned to each digit or position in a group of characters.

T F 19. Mark-sense cards and Port-A-Punch cards are common means of unit record data input.

T F 20. The purpose of verifying is to see that the original data has been accurately punched into the card.

MATCHING STATEMENTS Select the matching description for each term from the list on the right.

_____ 1.	EAM cycle	a. Group of related records
_____ 2.	Verify	b. Vertical group of punches
_____ 3.	Mark sense	c. Modification of Hollerith code
_____ 4.	Summary record	d. Input—Processing—Output
_____ 5.	Column	e. Graphic residue
_____ 6.	File	f. Predetermined number of columns
_____ 7.	Activity record	g. Check accuracy
_____ 8.	EBCDIC	h. X punch
_____ 9.	Fixed-length record	i. Condensed data
_____ 10.	11 zone	j. Detail card

MULTIPLE CHOICE STATEMENTS Circle the correct answer or answers for each statement.

1. The Hollerith card was first used in
   a. 1870
   b. 1880
   c. 1890
   d. 1900

2. The EAM cycle consists of
   a. input, processing, output
   b. processing, recording, output
   c. output, input, processing
   d. processing, output, input

3. In the unit record system
   a. several pieces of data refer to same item
   b. the standard punched card is used
   c. one transaction is on a single card
   d. all of above

4. Which of the following are advantages of unit record cards?
   a. convenient for people to handle
   b. 80 columns wide
   c. may be written upon
   d. moderate equipment costs

5. Which of the following are synonyms for the Hollerith card?
   a. tab card
   b. unit record card
   c. IBM card
   d. logical card

6. A standard punched card contains
   a. nine digit rows and four zone rows
   b. ten digit rows and three zone rows
   c. nine digit rows and three zone rows
   d. ten digit rows and four zone rows

7. The 11 zone is sometimes called
   a. the X punch
   b. the Y punch
   c. the zero punch
   d. none of above

8. Which of the following describe(s) a summary record?
   a. a detail record
   b. record layout
   c. report from other records
   d. variable-length record

9. Which of the following are used to differentiate files?
   a. card size
   b. card color
   c. color stripe
   d. corner cut

10. Which of the following are methods of data input?
    a. mark-sense card
    b. Port-A-Punch card
    c. System/3 card
    d. all of the above

SHORT ESSAY QUESTIONS

1. Compare the Hollerith code and EBCDIC code.

2. Describe the System/3 card and code.

3. Contrast the functions of the master record and detail record.

4. Summarize the function of the verifying machine.

5. Summarize three commonly used types of coding systems.

6. Contrast the layout and form of the System/3 card with the standard 80-column card.

7. Discuss the unit record method of data processing. Include advantages and limitations.

ANSWERS TO SELF-TESTS

1.	F	11.	T	1.	d	1.	c
2.	T	12.	T	2.	g	2.	a
3.	T	13.	T	3.	e	3.	d
4.	F	14.	F	4.	i	4.	a, c, d
5.	T	15.	F	5.	b	5.	a, b, c
6.	F	16.	T	6.	a	6.	c
7.	F	17.	F	7.	j	7.	a
8.	T	18.	T	8.	c	8.	c
9.	T	19.	T	9.	f	9.	b, c, d
10.	T	20.	T	10.	h	10.	d

Sorting and Collating

VOCABULARY Briefly define the following terms.

1. Numerical sorting

2. Alphabetic sorting

3. Grouping

4. Merging

5. Merging with selection

6. Matching

7. Checking sequence

8. Blank-column detection

9.   Single-column selection

10.   Search

SELF-TESTS

TRUE AND FALSE STATEMENTS

T   F   1.   Numerical sorting involves merging two files and pulling aside cards without matches.

T   F   2.   In blank-column detection, the machine determines whether a value has been punched in a specified field in each record.

T   F   3.   In sequence checking, files are not physically rearranged.

T   F   4.   A search is the process of checking through a file to locate a specific record.

T   F   5.   The sorter is designed to merge two files.

T   F   6.   A reverse digit sort requires as many passes through the machine as there are columns.

T   F   7.   Merging may not be performed on the collating machine.

T   F   8.   The sorting machine contains both primary and secondary feed hoppers.

T   F   9.   Matching can be performed on the sorting machine.

T   F   10.   In the collator, cards fed from the primary hopper pass under two sets of brushes.

T   F   11.   The collator is used to determine whether cards in a file are in their proper order.

T   F   12.   A numeric sort with a digit field eight columns wide would require eight passes through the sorter.

T   F   13.   It is sometimes faster to manually select a required card from a small file than to use machines or computers.

T   F   14.   Before merging with selection, two files are present. After merging with selection, three files are present.

T   F   15.   In merging two files, the files need not be in alphabetic or numeric order.

T   F   16.   A master file and a detail card file are often brought together in a single file in a process called merging.

T   F   17.   Organizing cards into related categories, such as names of individuals, date, or item, is an example of grouping.

T   F   18.   Sorting and collating may be done manually or by unit record, but not by computer.

T   F   19.   Collating machines perform merging, matching, and blank-column detection.

T   F   20.   A file may, or may not, contain the object of the search.

MATCHING STATEMENTS Select the matching description for each term from the list on the right.

_____	1.	Primary hopper	a.	Feeds primary files
_____	2.	Merging with selection	b.	Sequential order file
_____	3.	Alphabetic sorting	c.	Sorting machine
_____	4.	Reverse digit sort	d.	Requires two passes per column
_____	5.	Search	e.	Right-hand column sorted first
_____	6.	Single-column selection	f.	Locate object
_____	7.	Checking sequence	g.	Pull aside unmatched cards
_____	8.	Merging	h.	Collating machine
_____	9.	Four receiving card pockets	i.	Combining two files into one
_____	10.	13 receiving pockets	j.	X punch

MULTIPLE CHOICE STATEMENTS Circle the correct answer or answers for each statement.

1. A unit record machine can process about
   a. 10,000 cards per minute
   b. 5,000 cards per minute
   c. 2,000 cards per minute
   d. 1,000 cards per minute

2. Unit record and manual methods rely upon
   a. conversion into electronic pulses
   b. speed measured in nanoseconds
   c. physical movement of cards
   d. none of the above

3. Blank-column detection
   a. detects gross pay on master records
   b. flags all master records
   c. flags records containing blank columns
   d. punches data in blank columns

4. In grouping
   a. records are in no specific order at the beginning
   b. like data is next to each other upon completion
   c. files are arranged by categories
   d. all of the above

5. The operation of merging involves
   a. combining two files into a single file
   b. after merging, two files are present
   c. before merging, four files are present
   d. none of the above

25

6. Which is *not* a characteristic of the sorting machine?
   a. machine sorts, sequences, and column selects
   b. receiving pockets
   c. six-digit counter
   d. processes cards at the rate of 10,000 per minute

7. Which of the following are performed on the collating machine?
   a. merging
   b. matching
   c. sorting
   d. punching

8. Matching differs from merging with selection in that
   a. cards are sorted alphabetically
   b. cards are sorted numerically
   c. matched cards from the two files are not merged
   d. none of the above

9. The function of checking sequence is to
   a. check spelling
   b. sort cards
   c. determine if cards are in proper order
   d. physically rearrange cards

10. The manual method of sorting is satisfactory for
    a. high-volume processing
    b. high-speed processing
    c. accuracy of processing
    d. small amounts of data

SHORT ESSAY QUESTIONS

1. When is it appropriate to use manual, unit record, and computer methods of collating and sorting?

2. Distinguish between the operations of merging and matching.

3. Discuss single-column selection and how it is used.

4. How do collating and sorting machines differ in function?

5. Describe how the X punch is used.

6. Describe the operation of merging with selection on the collator.

7. Describe the procedure for numerical sorting.

ANSWERS TO SELF-TESTS

1.	F	11.	T	1.	a	1.	c
2.	T	12.	T	2.	g	2.	c
3.	T	13.	T	3.	d	3.	c
4.	T	14.	T	4.	e	4.	d
5.	F	15.	F	5.	f	5.	a
6.	T	16.	T	6.	j	6.	d
7.	F	17.	T	7.	b	7.	a, b
8.	F	18.	F	8.	i	8.	c
9.	F	19.	T	9.	h	9.	c
10.	T	20.	T	10.	c	10.	d

Reproducing, Interpreting, and Reporting

VOCABULARY Briefly define the following terms.

1. Reproducing

2. Interpreting

3. Reporting

4. 80-80 reproducing

5. Selective reproducing

6. Offset reproducing

7. Gang punching

8. Mark-sense punching

9. End printing

10. Listing

SELF-TESTS

TRUE AND FALSE STATEMENTS

T   F   1. Interpreting involves duplicating records or files.

T   F   2. In 80-80 reproducing, selected fields are copied.

T   F   3. In offset reproducing, selected columns in a master record are punched into different columns on the detail record.

T   F   4. Gang punching involves copying data from a master card into one or more detail cards.

T   F   5. The operation of printing large letters on the end of a card is called mark sensing.

T   F   6. Calculating involves manipulation of data by arithmetic means and printing it out.

T   F   7. Printing is a form of reporting in which data is calculated and printed out on a sheet of paper.

T   F   8. Document-originating machines will interpret cards.

T   F   9. The interpreting machine moves cards past two sets of brushes and will print 80 columns across the card.

T   F   10. Both verifying and interpreting can always be performed on the same machines.

T   F   11. Unit record accounting machines perform listing and printing operations at the rate of 18,000 cards per minute.

T   F   12. There are 25 horizontal print positions available on the alphabetic interpreter.

T   F   13. In mark sensing, large letters are sensed by a character reader and converted into holes.

T   F   14. Gang punching involves copying data from one master card onto another.

T   F   15. Summary punching involves accumulating totals and punching the information into cards using the reproducing punch and the accounting machine.

T   F   16. In end printing, up to 60 characters may be printed along the end of the card.

T   F   17. The operation of listing 80 columns of information from a punched card onto a sheet of paper is called 80-80 reproducing.

T   F   18. Printing is a form of reporting that results in statements, forms, or other documents.

T   F   20. Mark-sense bubbles are converted into holes by an interpreting machine.

MATCHING STATEMENTS Select the matching description for each term from the list on the right.

_____	1.	Mark sensing	a.	Large display numbers
_____	2.	End printing	b.	Specified record in a file
_____	3.	Interpreting on keypunch	c.	Decoding holes
_____	4.	Performed on interpreting machine	d.	Arithmetic manipulation
_____	5.	Selective reproducing	e.	Outputting data
_____	6.	Field-selected reproducing	f.	Electrographic pencil
_____	7.	80-80 reproducing	g.	80 columns
_____	8.	Interpreting	h.	Copying 80 columns
_____	9.	Reporting	i.	60 columns
_____	10.	Calculating	j.	Specified columns in a record

MULTIPLE CHOICE STATEMENTS Circle the correct answer or answers for each statement.

1. Which of the following are characteristics of 80-80 reproducing?
   a. performed on reproducing punch
   b. original record punched into duplicate record
   c. 80 columns are reproduced
   d. data is interpreted as it is reproduced

2. Offset punching involves
   a. copying selected columns
   b. reproducing in different fields
   c. reproducing punch
   d. all of the above

3. One of the following is *not* a characteristic of gang punching.
   a. copying data from one master card into one or more detail cards
   b. single master card gang punching
   c. interspersed master card gang punching
   d. end printing

4. Interpreting involves
   a. translating symbols
   b. 80-80 reproducing
   c. 90 columns
   d. none of the above

5. Listing is the same as
   a. calculating
   b. detail printing
   c. reproducing
   d. none of the above

32

6. Which of the following are examples of reporting?

    a. restructuring data
    b. inputting data
    c. manipulating data
    d. printing reports

7. An interpreting machine can print data in any of

    a. 15 horizontal positions
    b. 20 horizontal positions
    c. 25 horizontal positions
    d. none of the above

8. Unit record accounting machines

    a. have 120 print wheels
    b. can print 18,000 characters per minute
    c. can process 150 cards per minute
    d. all of the above

9. Early unit record accounting machines used counters that were

    a. flip flop circuits
    b. flop flip circuits
    c. transistorized devices
    d. electromechanical devices

10. End printing involves

    a. inputting data
    b. sorting data
    c. printing letters on back of card
    d. printing letters on edge of card

SHORT ESSAY QUESTIONS

1. Describe the function of a document-originating machine.

2. How does end printing differ from interpreting?

3. Summarize the function of the interpreting machine.

4. How does 80-80 reproducing differ from 80-80 listing?

5. Describe the operation of reporting.

6. Describe the operation of offset reproducing.

7. What advantages does mark sensing have over keypunching?

ANSWERS TO SELF-TESTS

1.	F	11.	F	1.	f	1.	a, b, c
2.	F	12.	T	2.	a	2.	d
3.	T	13.	F	3.	g	3.	d
4.	T	14.	F	4.	i	4.	a
5.	F	15.	T	5.	b	5.	b
6.	F	16.	F	6.	j	6.	a, c, d
7.	F	17.	F	7.	h	7.	c
8.	F	18.	T	8.	c	8.	d
9.	F	19.	T	9.	e	9.	d
10.	F	20.	T	10.	d	10.	d

Fundamental Computer Concepts

VOCABULARY   Briefly define the following terms.

1.   Memory

2.   CPU

3.   Input system

4.   Output system

5.   Mainframe

6.   Primary storage

7.   I/O

8.   Compiler

9. Source program

10. Execution

SELF-TESTS

TRUE AND FALSE STATEMENTS

T F 1. Hardware refers to computer equipment, parts, machines, integrated circuits.

T F 2. Data is converted into electronic pulses in the CPU for transmission.

T F 3. The input system sends a string of pulses representing data to the CPU.

T F 4. Card readers, magnetic tape readers, and line printers are input devices.

T F 5. A console typewriter from which the operator directs the machine is sometimes attached to the CPU.

T F 6. Primary storage is sometimes called core output.

T F 7. The problem program is sometimes called the program deck and the data set, the data deck.

T F 8. Primary storage is reusable, fast, but not directly accessible to the control unit.

T F 9. Primary storage is used to store data that must be called in frequently.

T F 10. Line printers, card punches, and video tubes are examples of output devices.

T F 11. A telecommunications system is one of the subsystems of the computer.

T F 12. General-purpose computers are designed to perform a single, specific task.

T F 13. Minicomputers are small, desk-top, digital computers, with a CPU.

T F 14. Large computers have primary storage capacity of many millions of bytes.

T F 15. An Assembler program converts machine language instructions into language readable by the programmer.

T F 16. The process of converting instructions into machine language is called compilation.

T F 17. Execution is the process of storing a program ready for processing.

T F 18. Analog computers process quantities such as numbers or letters.

T F 19. Output from a digital computer usually is on a cathode ray tube or plotter.

T F 20. Computers may be classified by either their physical size or the number of I/O units they support.

MATCHING STATEMENTS Select the matching description for each term from the list on the right.

———	1.	Minicomputer	a.	Input unit
———	2.	Output	b.	Translates instructions
———	3.	Multiprocessing	c.	Letters and numbers
———	4.	Digital computer	d.	Computer subsystem
———	5.	Analog computer	e.	Desk-top device
———	6.	Audio response unit	f.	2 or more CPU's
———	7.	Card reader	g.	Output unit
———	8.	Primary storage	h.	Continuous form
———	9.	Data set	i.	Data deck
———	10.	Compiler	j.	Core storage

MULTIPLE CHOICE STATEMENTS Circle the correct answer or answers for each statement.

1. Which of the following are computer subsystems?
   a. input system
   b. telecommunications system
   c. costing system
   d. output system

2. A digital computer can process information as
   a. letters and numbers
   b. visual wave form
   c. electrical voltage
   d. all of the above

3. Which of the following are characteristic of the general-purpose computer?
   a. digital or analog in nature
   b. performs specific single tasks
   c. versatile system
   d. stores a program for execution

4. Which of the following are characteristics of a minicomputer?
   a. 250K storage
   b. costs under $25,000
   c. limited I/O devices
   d. uses teletype devices

5. Small computers have storage capacities of
   a. under 4K bytes
   b. between 8 and 12K bytes
   c. over 32K bytes
   d. none of the above

6. Desk-top computers with storage capacities under 8K are
   a. minicomputers
   b. small computers
   c. medium-sized computers
   d. large computers

7. A computer with a storage capacity of many millions of bytes would be classified as a
   a. minicomputer
   b. small computer
   c. medium-sized computer
   d. large computer

8. Computers can only process data as
   a. equipment language
   b. hardware language
   c. machine language
   d. scanner language

9. In computer problem solving, the computer must be given
   a. location of data
   b. explicit instructions
   c. logic to follow
   d. all of the above

10. One of the following is *not* a characteristic of compilers.
    a. written by programmer who is user
    b. generates many lines of instructions
    c. converts instructions into machine language
    d. serves one language

SHORT ESSAY QUESTIONS

1. Describe the function of the computer's input system.

2. Describe the function of the central processing unit.

3. Describe the function of the output system.

4. What are the major steps taken in solving a problem on the computer?

5. Discuss the advantages of the stored program.

6. Contrast the ways in which humans and computers solve problems.

7. Describe the function of the compiler.

ANSWERS TO SELF-TESTS

1.	T	11.	T	1.	e	1.	a, b, d
2.	F	12.	F	2.	d	2.	a
3.	T	13.	T	3.	f	3.	a, c, d
4.	F	14.	T	4.	c	4.	b, c, d
5.	T	15.	F	5.	h	5.	b
6.	F	16.	T	6.	g	6.	a
7.	T	17.	F	7.	a	7.	d
8.	F	18.	F	8.	j	8.	c
9.	T	19.	F	9.	i	9.	d
10.	T	20.	T	10.	b	10.	a

Data Input

VOCABULARY   Briefly define the following terms.

1.   I/O channel

2.   Channel address

3.   Channel scheduler

4.   Queuing

5.   Fixed channel

6.   Floating channel

7.   On-line input

8.   Control unit

9. Buffering

10. Multiplexing

SELF-TESTS

TRUE AND FALSE STATEMENTS

T F 1. On-line input devices are wired directly to the CPU and transmit pulses from a record.

T F 2. Control units regulate the timing of the I/O machine, relieving the burden from the CPU.

T F 3. Data input devices print out forms.

T F 4. Paper tape readers optically scan a character and convert it to an electrical pulse.

T F 5. An MICR device scans images printed from a special magnetic ink.

T F 6. The console typewriter, though slow, is both an input and output device.

T F 7. MICR devices cannot recognize handwritten or printed numbers.

T F 8. Paper tape readers convert holes in paper tapes to electronic pulses relayed to the CPU.

T F 9. The channel address refers to the location of a byte of data on a piece of magnetic tape.

T F 10. Floating channels are permanently wired to a single group of devices.

T F 11. Overlapping allows the CPU to input, process, and output data simultaneously.

T F 12. Magnetic drum storage and data cell storage devices are both slow devices.

T F 13. Multiplexing is the process of placing waiting jobs in line until an input/output device is available.

T F 14. Multiplexer channels feed data between peripheral devices.

T F 15. Selector channels are used to feed data from high-speed devices directly to the CPU.

T F 16. The three common input channels are called multiplexers, triplexers, and selectors.

T F 17. Line printers, card punches, and console typewriters are slow devices.

T F 18. In buffering, data is held in storage and fed to the CPU in a burst.

T F 19. A maximum of two I/O channels may be connected to the CPU at any one time.

T F 20. In the sense brush card reader, light is passed through the card and picked up by a photocell.

MATCHING STATEMENTS Select the matching description for each term from the list on the right.

_____	1.	Pulse train	a.	Photocell
_____	2.	Control units	b.	Unique number
_____	3.	Senses holes	c.	Queues jobs
_____	4.	OCR	d.	Magnetic ink
_____	5.	MICR	e.	Console typewriter
_____	6.	Attached to CPU	f.	Assigned by demand
_____	7.	Channel address	g.	Permanently assigned
_____	8.	Channel scheduler	h.	Character scanner
_____	9.	Fixed channel	i.	String of bits
_____	10.	Floating channel	j.	Regulate timing of I/O machines

MULTIPLE CHOICE STATEMENTS Circle the correct answer or answers for each statement.

1. One of the following is *not* a characteristic of on-line input devices.
   a. wired to the CPU
   b. transmits pulse train
   c. records data on tape
   d. converts holes in a card to a signal

2. Which of the following are characteristics of card readers?
   a. equipped with card hopper
   b. punching dies
   c. read station
   d. photocell

3. The optical character reader
   a. converts data to mechanical pulses
   b. scans optical images
   c. scans magnetic characters
   d. none of the above

4. OCR machines read in data from
   a. utility bills
   b. adding machine tapes
   c. magnetic tapes
   d. punched tapes

5. One of the following is *not* a characteristic of the console typewriter.
   a. connected off-line to the CPU
   b. receives messages from the operator
   c. transmits messages from the CPU
   d. is a very slow I/O device

6. The function of the tape pooler is to convert characters on magnetic tape to
   a. tightly spaced characters
   b. widely spaced characters
   c. no affect on character spacing
   d. none of the above

7. Mechanical selector switches were replaced by
   a. toggle switches
   b. knife switches
   c. push buttons
   d. electronic switching arrangements

8. The limitation of single access to the CPU
   a. was common to early computers
   b. limited speed of I/O
   c. was solved by electronic switching
   d. all of the above

9. A channel address is
   a. a mechanical selector switch
   b. a multiplexer selector switch
   c. an electronic switch
   d. none of the above

10. One of the following is *not* a slow device.
    a. line printer
    b. console typewriter
    c. magnetic disk drive
    d. card punch

SHORT ESSAY QUESTIONS

1. Describe the function of control units in the input system.

2. How do optical character scanners differ from magnetic ink recognition devices?

3. Describe a typical channel addressing system.

4. Contrast fixed and floating channels.

5. Describe the process by which the card reader senses holes in a card.

6. Describe the concept of multiplexing.

7. Summarize the advantages of buffering devices.

ANSWERS TO SELF-TESTS

1.	T	11.	T	1.	i	1.	c
2.	T	12.	F	2.	j	2.	a,c,d
3.	F	13.	F	3.	a	3.	b
4.	F	14.	F	4.	h	4.	a,b
5.	T	15.	T	5.	d	5.	a
6.	T	16.	F	6.	e	6.	a
7.	F	17.	T	7.	b	7.	d
8.	T	18.	T	8.	c	8.	d
9.	F	19.	F	9.	g	9.	d
10.	F	20.	F	10.	f	10.	c

Data Representation and Computer Arithmetic

VOCABULARY Briefly define the following terms.

1. Place value

2. Decimal system

3. Binary

4. Hexadecimal

5. Binary coded decimal

6. EBCDIC

7. Even parity

8. Odd parity

9. Channel

10. Track

SELF-TESTS

TRUE AND FALSE STATEMENTS

T F 1. In written communication, symbols such as numbers, letters, or codes stand for objects or events.

T F 2. Man's earliest attempt at data representation involved Arabic numerals.

T F 3. The base of a numbering system is the number of states it recognizes.

T F 4. In the base 10 system, ten states, represented by the digits 0, 1, 2, 3, 4, 5, 6, 7, 8, 9, are used.

T F 5. The hexadecimal system is sometimes called base 8.

T F 6. The first four binary place values are: 6, 4, 2, 1.

T F 7. In binary representation, the symbols 0, 1, 2 are used.

T F 8. In binary addition, 1 + 1 = 0, with 1 to carry.

T F 9. In binary subtraction, 1 − 0 = 0

T F 10. The computer uses the two's complement when performing binary addition.

T F 11. Hexadecimal to decimal conversion is most easily accomplished using manual binary calculations.

T F 12. The Baudot code was widely used on magnetic tape.

T F 13. ASCII uses no parity check bit.

T F 14. In longitudinal parity, a check of the bits is made across the width of the tape.

T F 15. Intelligence channels transmit parity bit information.

T F 16. In even parity a check bit is placed with each uneven byte to make the sum even.

T F 17. A bit consists of a group of bytes.

T F 18. Two decimal numbers can be packed in one byte using EBCDIC.

T F 19. In odd parity, the sum of the bits is always even.

T F 20. ASCII is widely used at the present time to transmit data to computers.

MATCHING STATEMENTS Select the matching description for each term from the list on the right.

_____	1. Baudot	a.	Extension of Baudot code
_____	2. ASCII	b.	Modern 8-channel code

_____	3.	EBCDIC	c.	Base 16
_____	4.	TWX	d.	Base 2
_____	5.	Data conversion	e.	Sum along length of tape
_____	6.	Hexadecimal	f.	Even sum of bits
_____	7.	Decimal	g.	Base 10
_____	8.	Binary	h.	Hex to binary
_____	9.	Even parity	i.	Modern 9-channel code
_____	10.	Longitudinal parity	j.	Telegraph code

MULTIPLE CHOICE STATEMENTS Circle the correct answer or answers for each statement.

1. Place values in the decimal system include
   a. 100's, 10's, 1's
   b. 10's, 1's, 0's
   c. 0, 1, 2, 3, 4, 5, 6, 7, 8, 9
   d. none of the above

2. Place values in the binary system include
   a. 12, 8, 4, 2
   b. 4, 3, 2, 1
   c. 8, 4, 2, 1
   d. none of the above

3. In binary addition, 0 + 1 equals
   a. 0
   b. 1
   c. 1 + 1 to carry
   d. none of the above

4. In binary subtraction, 1 − 0 equals
   a. 0
   b. 1
   c. 2
   d. none of the above

5. In the binary system, hexadecimal E is equivalent to
   a. 0010
   b. 1110
   c. 1010
   d. 1111

6. In the decimal system, hexadecimal 11A is equal to
   a. 256
   b. 282
   c. 356
   d. none of the above

7. The decimal value of hexadecimal CAB is
    a. 256
    b. 4156
    c. 3243
    d. none of the above

8. The decimal value of binary 1110101 is
    a. 105
    b. 107
    c. 127
    d. none of the above

9. Which of the following are *not* hexadecimal numbers?
    a. 1111
    b. FACE
    c. CASE
    d. BEBE

10. Which of the following are *not* acceptable binary numbers?
    a. 1010 1010
    b. 1212 1212
    c. 1111 0000
    d. 0000 0000

SHORT ESSAY QUESTIONS

1. Describe how the binary system differs from the hexadecimal system.

2. What is the purpose of the parity check bit?

3. Discuss why binary representation is ideal for "two-state" devices such as computing machines.

4. How do tracks differ from channels?

5. Describe the odd parity system and how it is used to detect loss of bits.

6. Describe the even parity system and how it is used to detect loss of bits.

ANSWERS TO SELF-TESTS

1. T	11. F	1. j	1. a
2. F	12. F	2. b	2. c
3. T	13. F	3. i	3. b
4. T	14. F	4. a	4. b
5. F	15. F	5. h	5. b
6. F	16. T	6. c	6. b
7. F	17. F	7. g	7. c
8. T	18. T	8. d	8. d
9. F	19. F	9. f	9. c
10. F	20. T	10. e	10. b

The Central Processing Unit: Functions and Components

VOCABULARY Briefly define the following terms.

1. Core storage

2. Sense wire

3. Selected core

4. X and Y wires

5. Storage address

6. Registers

7. Cycle clock

8. Counter

9. Decoder

10. Gates

SELF-TESTS

TRUE AND FALSE STATEMENTS

T   F   1.   Primary storage is sometimes called secondary storage.

T   F   2.   The advantage of primary storage is its reusability and fast access time.

T   F   3.   Primary storage is relatively low in cost and, hence, most computers have large primary storage capacities.

T   F   4.   Core storage is composed of about 100 ferrite cores, assembled on a rod, forming a network.

T   F   5.   Data is read into core using the X and sense wires.

T   F   6.   Data is read out of core using the sense wire.

T   F   7.   Computers can be built to store either fixed- or variable-length words, but not both.

T   F   8.   The data stored in a given location is the same as its address.

T   F   9.   Registers are similar to core storage, but hold only a few bytes of data.

T   F   10.   The function of the instruction register is to hold the instruction address.

T   F   11.   Accumulator registers hold binary bits, such as numbers, sums, and quotients.

T   F   12.   Counters are transistor or diode devices, not mechanical devices.

T   F   13.   Logic gates are used to compare values.

T   F   14.   The instruction cycle always precedes the execution cycle.

T   F   15.   The instruction cycle is sometimes called the I Cycle and the time spent is called I Time.

T   F   16.   During E Time, operation codes are sent to instruction registers.

T   F   17.   The cycle clock emits electrical pulses.

T   F   18.   Computer instructions are composed of two parts: the operation code and the internal code.

T   F   19.   The op code stands for the operation to be performed.

T   F   20.   Storage registers are permanent storage devices that hold computer programs.

MATCHING STATEMENTS Select the matching description for each term from the list on the right.

_____	1.	Ferrite core	a.	Execution cycle
_____	2.	Word mark	b.	Operation
_____	3.	Accumulator register	c.	Beginning of word
_____	4.	E Time	d.	Holds sum
_____	5.	Op code	e.	Location
_____	6.	Selected core	f.	Converts instructions
_____	7.	Storage address	g.	Primary storage
_____	8.	Decoder	h.	Magnetized core
_____	9.	Sense wire	i.	Group of ferrite cores
_____	10.	Core plane	j.	Read out

MULTIPLE CHOICE STATEMENTS Circle the correct answer or answers for each statement.

1. One of the following is *not* a characteristic of primary storage.
   a. reusability
   b. low cost
   c. limited capacity
   d. fast access time

2. Core storage is composed of
   a. thousands of wires
   b. thousands of resistors
   c. thousands of ferrite cores
   d. none of the above

3. When a core is magnetized in a clockwise direction, it is said to represent
   a. zero state
   b. one state
   c. binary state
   d. none of the above

4. One of the following is *not* strung through cores.
   a. sense wire
   b. circumference wire
   c. Y wire
   d. X wire

5. A computer word is composed of
   a. many transistors in one location
   b. many op codes
   c. all bits in one location
   d. none of the above

6. A machine in which each word has its own address is called
    a. bit addressable
    b. byte addressable
    c. character addressable
    d. word addressable

7. Registers are similar in nature to
    a. core storage, but more limited
    b. cycle clock
    c. decoders
    d. none of the above

8. The function of the instruction counter is to
    a. decode operations
    b. keep track of instructions
    c. store instructions
    d. flip flop instructions

9. Which of the following are registers found in computers?
    a. address register
    b. storage register
    c. question register
    d. instruction register

10. Logic gates *cannot* test which of the following concepts.
    a. part of
    b. less than
    c. equal to
    d. greater than

SHORT ESSAY QUESTIONS

1. Discuss the composition of primary storage.

2. Describe core storage addressing.

3. Summarize the functions of registers.

4. Discuss the functions of the I and E Cycles.

5. Discuss how data is read into core.

6. Summarize the distinctions between data stored in a location and its address.

7. Discuss how gates are used in a CPU.

ANSWERS TO SELF-TESTS

1.	F	11.	T	1.	g	1.	b
2.	T	12.	T	2.	c	2.	c
3.	F	13.	T	3.	d	3.	b
4.	F	14.	T	4.	a	4.	b
5.	F	15.	T	5.	b	5.	c
6.	T	16.	F	6.	h	6.	d
7.	F	17.	T	7.	e	7.	a
8.	F	18.	F	8.	f	8.	b
9.	T	19.	T	9.	j	9.	a,b,d
10.	F	20.	F	10.	i	10.	a

Secondary Storage Systems

VOCABULARY Briefly define the following terms.

1. Access time

2. Sequential access

3. Random access

4. File maintenance

5. Tape record

6. Load-point mark

7. End-of-reel mark

8. Sector

9. File protection ring

10. Secondary storage

SELF-TESTS

TRUE AND FALSE STATEMENTS

T   F   1.   Primary storage is indirectly accessible to the CPU.

T   F   2.   Magnetic disk storage uses a thin ribbon of plastic coated with a ferromagnetic compound.

T   F   3.   Data is read from, or recorded on, magnetic drum devices, using magnetic read/write heads.

T   F   4.   The data cell is a major form of secondary storage.

T   F   5.   Secondary storage devices can be wired together to expand available capacity.

T   F   6.   Average access time is relatively constant among secondary storage devices.

T   F   7.   Access time is a function of location and amount of data and speed of device.

T   F   8.   Sequential access enables data to be pulled from storage based upon its location and address.

T   F   9.   Random access requires that each item in the file be searched in sequence.

T   F   10.   Magnetic tape may require several seconds to locate a piece of data.

T   F   11.   Magnetic drum may require from 8 to 95 seconds to locate data.

T   F   12.   The advantage of secondary storage is its high capacity and low cost.

T   F   13.   Magnetic tape has a slower average access time than magnetic disk.

T   F   14.   Magnetic drum has a greater storage capacity than data cell drive.

T   F   15.   Magnetic tape is an example of sequential access.

T   F   16.   Magnetic disk is an example of random access.

T   F   17.   The IRG is a space of about four inches between bytes of data.

T   F   18.   The end of a reel of tape is marked by a load-point mark.

T   F   19.   When the file protection ring is removed, no new data can be recorded on the tape.

T   F   20.   The pie-shaped sector on a disk pack is called a cylinder.

MATCHING STATEMENTS Select the matching description for each term from the list on the right.

_____	1.	Magnetic disk	a.	Beginning of tape
_____	2.	Magnetic tape	b.	Storage address
_____	3.	Magnetic drum	c.	Round plate
_____	4.	Data cell	d.	Ribbon of plastic
_____	5.	Random access	e.	Space between records
_____	6.	Sequential access	f.	Retrieval time
_____	7.	Access time	g.	End of tape
_____	8.	Load-point mark	h.	Metal cylinder
_____	9.	End-of-reel mark	i.	Search in sequence
_____	10.	IRG	j.	Strips

MULTIPLE CHOICE STATEMENTS Circle the correct answer or answers for each statement.

1. Which of the following are random access devices?
   a. magnetic tape
   b. magnetic drum
   c. magnetic disk
   d. data cell

2. Which of the following is *not* a function of access time?
   a. kind of data
   b. amount of data
   c. location of data
   d. speed of device

3. Which are advantages of secondary storage?
   a. direct accessibility
   b. high capacity
   c. low cost
   d. flexibility

4. The average access time for magnetic tape is
   a. 5 milliseconds
   b. 5 microseconds
   c. 5 seconds
   d. none of the above

5. The average access time for data cell drive is
   a. 350 seconds
   b. 350 microseconds
   c. 350 milliseconds
   d. none of the above

6. Average access time is a function of
   a. cost of data
   b. speed of operator
   c. location of data
   d. speed of hardware

7. Which method(s) is(are) used to access data from secondary storage?
   a. internal access
   b. sequential access
   c. external access
   d. random access

8. The concentric circles around which data is recorded on a magnetic disk are called
   a. sectors
   b. cylinders
   c. tracks
   d. none of the above

9. Which device uses read/write heads?
   a. disk storage
   b. drum storage
   c. magnetic tape storage
   d. all of the above

10. The purpose of the file protection ring is to
    a. prevent unreeling tape
    b. prevent punching tape
    c. prevent accidental erasing of tape
    d. prevent theft of tape

SHORT ESSAY QUESTIONS

1. What are the advantages of secondary storage?

2. Describe the process by which data is recorded on magnetic tape.

3. Explain the difference between random access and sequential access.

4. In random access devices, what is the relationship between storage capacity and access time?

5. What is an IRG? Discuss its function.

6. Discuss how data is recorded on magnetic disk.

7. Describe the purpose and task of file maintenance.

ANSWERS TO SELF-TESTS

1.	F	11.	F	1.	c	1.	b,c,d
2.	F	12.	T	2.	d	2.	a
3.	T	13.	T	3.	h	3.	b,c,d
4.	T	14.	F	4.	j	4.	c
5.	T	15.	T	5.	b	5.	c
6.	F	16.	T	6.	i	6.	c,d
7.	T	17.	F	7.	f	7.	b,d
8.	F	18.	F	8.	a	8.	c
9.	F	19.	T	9.	g	9.	d
10.	T	20.	F	10.	e	10.	c

Data Output

VOCABULARY Briefly define the following terms.

1. On-line output devices

2. Off-line output devices

3. Buffering

4. Spooling

5. Serial printing

6. Parallel printing

7. Train printer

8. Wire matrix

9. Cathode ray tube

10. Thermal imaging

SELF-TESTS

TRUE AND FALSE STATEMENTS

T   F   1.   Plotters, audio response units, and paper tape punches are all data output devices.

T   F   2.   In on-line output, data is transmitted directly to the output record without being held in intermediate storage.

T   F   3.   The type bar printer is slow and not suitable for high-volume output.

T   F   4.   Card punches can punch up to 5,000 cards per minute.

T   F   5.   The video display stations are examples of plotter output devices.

T   F   6.   A video display console displays letter forms on a cathode ray tube.

T   F   7.   A video display terminal is an example of a type wheel printer.

T   F   8.   An audio response unit generates words and phrases from prerecorded information on a direct access storage device.

T   F   9.   Phototypesetter machines have interchangeable type disks that hold three fonts of type each.

T   F   10.   The principles of buffering and multiplexing and speed differences in data output are similar to those in data input.

T   F   11.   A system is said to be I/O bound when the CPU limits the throughput.

T   F   12.   Buffering is less important in data output than in data input.

T   F   13.   In spooling, a single line printer is attached to a magnetic drum storage device.

T   F   14.   Off-line I/O is a means of breaking the I/O bottleneck.

T   F   15.   The type spool and type bar are examples of common printing techniques.

T   F   16.   In photographic imaging, a cathode ray tube and electrostatic devices are used to generate letter forms.

T   F   17.   In serial printing, a line of 100 characters would be printed letter by letter, from left to right.

T   F   18.   A common wire matrix printer uses 350 wire rods arranged in a pattern.

T   F   19.   In parallel printing, a line 100 characters wide would be printed from a type element that moves across the sheet.

T   F   20.   The cathode ray tube employs an electron beam that is scanned back and forth over a coated surface.

MATCHING STATEMENTS Select the matching description for each term from the list on the right.

_____	1.	Font	a.	Rotate to character
_____	2.	Plotter	b.	Cathode ray tube
_____	3.	Wire matrix printer	c.	Keypunch machines
_____	4.	Buffering	d.	Typewriter principle
_____	5.	Train printer	e.	Spoken word
_____	6.	Audio response unit	f.	X, Y axis
_____	7.	Video display unit	g.	Photographic imaging
_____	8.	Phototypesetter	h.	High-speed output
_____	9.	Typebar	i.	Set of characters
_____	10.	Typewheel	j.	Intermediate storage

MULTIPLE CHOICE STATEMENTS Circle the correct answer or answers for each statement.

1. One of the following is *not* a common output device.
   a. paper tape punch
   b. card punch
   c. card reader
   d. plotter

2. A device that creates images on a video tube is called
   a. magnetic disk
   b. audio response unit
   c. line printer
   d. none of the above

3. Audio response units output data as
   a. spoken word
   b. printed word
   c. magnetic disk
   d. type bar

4. Which of the following are output from plotters?
   a. spoken word
   b. light pen
   c. graphic shapes
   d. curves and figures

5. The function of a phototypesetter is to
   a. generate newspaper text
   b. generate book text
   c. record magnetic tape
   d. none of the above

6. One of the following is *not* a common means of forming letter images.
   a. type scroll
   b. type bar
   c. type element
   d. type wheel

7. One of the following is a characteristic of cathode ray tube display.
   a. uses print wheels
   b. produces permanent record
   c. produces audio record
   d. produces nonpermanent record

8. When a system's throughput is limited by the I/O devices, it is said to be
   a. spoolbound
   b. CPU bound
   c. I/O bound
   d. none of the above

9. The function of buffering is to
   a. hold bytes in permantent storage
   b. align characters along margin
   c. hold characters in temporary storage
   d. none of the above

10. To increase throughput, some computers use
    a. card only input
    b. paper tape only input
    c. magnetic tape only input
    d. none of the above

SHORT ESSAY QUESTIONS

1. Discuss the principles of on-line and off-line output devices.

2. Describe how phototypesetting machines form images.

3. Describe how audio response units output data.

4. Contrast how letters are formed using a type element with how they are formed using a wire matrix.

5. Describe how plotters output data.

6. Contrast serial and parallel printing.

7. Discuss the principle of buffering and how it breaks the I/O bottleneck.

ANSWERS TO SELF-TESTS

1.	T	11.	F	1.	i	1.	c
2.	T	12.	F	2.	f	2.	d
3.	T	13.	F	3.	c	3.	a
4.	F	14.	T	4.	j	4.	c,d
5.	F	15.	F	5.	h	5.	a,b
6.	T	16.	F	6.	e	6.	a
7.	F	17.	T	7.	b	7.	d
8.	T	18.	F	8.	g	8.	c
9.	T	19.	F	9.	d	9.	c
10.	T	20.	T	10.	a	10.	c

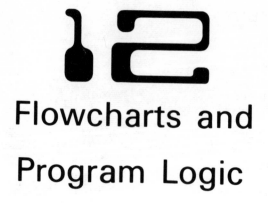

Flowcharts and Program Logic

VOCABULARY Briefly define the following terms.

1. System flowchart

2. Modular program flowchart

3. Detail program flowchart

4. Algorithm

5. Single-pass computation

6. Branching

7. Loop

8. Last-record loop

9. Limited loop

10. Process symbol

SELF-TESTS

TRUE AND FALSE STATEMENTS

T   F   1.   A system flowchart shows the relationship of various departments and work stations to the whole.

T   F   2.   Program flowcharts may be grouped into two categories: modular and detail.

T   F   3.   Modular program flowcharts show step-by-step details, including each minute branch in the program.

T   F   4.   STOP, START, or PAUSE is usually drawn in the center of a terminal symbol.

T   F   5.   The decision symbol, which indicates a branch or decision point, is diamond-shaped.

T   F   6.   The process symbol is a parallelogram used to show input or output.

T   F   7.   The document symbol, resembling a piece of paper, indicates that a hard-copy document is to be generated.

T   F   8.   Flowcharts are verbal descriptions of data flow.

T   F   9.   Normally, there is only one algorithm to solve a problem.

T   F   10.   The number of times a loop is executed can be limited by a loop with counter.

T   F   11.   In a limited loop, the programmer sets the maximum number of times it will be executed.

T   F   12.   A series of mathematical calculations can easily be repeated by the single-pass computation.

T   F   13.   A calculation to compute the interest on one loan would best be done using a loop with counter.

T   F   14.   Descriptive words are usually written outside the relevant flowchart symbols.

T   F   15.   The decision symbol is used to illustrate a branch with two or more paths.

T   F   16.   The punched card symbol may be used in place of the general I/O symbol if data is to be read from a punched card.

T   F   17.   Algorithms are usually drawn up after the problem has been keypunched and run.

T   F   18.   Connectors are used to show decision points.

T   F   19.   A calculation such as "find square root" is usually shown in a process box.

T   F   20.   A communications link shows data is being transferred from one location to another.

MATCHING STATEMENTS Select the matching description for each term from the list on the right.

———	1. System flowchart	a. START
———	2. Modular flowchart	b. Diamond shaped
———	3. Block flowchart	c. Overview
———	4. Terminal	d. Micro diagram
———	5. Calculation	e. Program logic
———	6. Decision	f. Increments each pass
———	7. Document	g. Block diagram
———	8. Algorithm	h. Process
———	9. Last-record loop	i. Hard copy
———	10. Loop with counter	j. Test data set

MULTIPLE CHOICE STATEMENTS Circle the correct answer or answers for each statement.

1. Which of the following are functions of a system flowchart?
   a. show people
   b. show documents
   c. show activities
   d. show programming detail

2. Which of the following are functions of the detail program flowchart?
   a. show steps in sequence
   b. present microscopic view
   c. show people
   d. show decision points

3. Which of the following words are shown in a terminal symbol?
   a. ADVANCE
   b. START
   c. STOP
   d. HALT

4. Which of the following are shown in a process block?
   a. read payroll
   b. multiply by cost
   c. calculate tax
   d. square root

5. One of the following is *not* a standard flowcharting symbol.
   a. connector
   b. magnetic tape
   c. direct access device
   d. delivery

6. Which program logic is best suited to repeat a cycle, counting each time it is executed?
   a. single-pass computation
   b. last-pass computation
   c. computation with counter
   d. loop with counter

7. Which of the following sets the maximum number of times a limited loop will be executed?
   a. the line printer
   b. the programmer
   c. the data
   d. none of the above

8. The end of a data deck is usually marked by
   a. a header card
   b. a trailer card
   c. load-point mark
   d. none of the above

9. An algorithm usually illustrates
   a. program cost
   b. programming time
   c. program logic
   d. none of the above

10. The trailer card is usually placed
    a. at the beginning of the data deck
    b. at the end of the data deck
    c. at the beginning of the program
    d. at the end of the program

SHORT ESSAY QUESTIONS

1. Contrast the functions of the system and program flowcharts.

2. How do decision symbols differ in function from process symbols?

3. What is the function of a decision table? How is it used?

4. Contrast the advantages of decision tables and flowcharts in describing program flow.

5. How does a last-record loop differ from a loop with counter?

6. What are algorithms? How are they used in solving data processing problems?

7. Describe the logic followed in branching to parallel tracks.

ANSWERS TO SELF-TESTS

1. T	11. T	1. c	1. a,b,c
2. T	12. F	2. g	2. a,b,d
3. F	13. F	3. d	3. b,c,d
4. T	14. F	4. a	4. b,c,d
5. T	15. T	5. h	5. d
6. F	16. T	6. b	6. d
7. T	17. F	7. i	7. b
8. F	18. F	8. e	8. b
9. F	19. T	9. j	9. c
10. T	20. T	10. f	10. b

Implementing the Program

VOCABULARY Briefly define the following terms.

1. Stand-alone program

2. Coding

3. Job control cards

4. Debugging

5. Compilation error

6. Execution error

7. Diagnostic message

8. Documentation

9. Abstract

10. Run manual

SELF-TESTS

TRUE AND FALSE STATEMENTS

T   F   1. The stand-alone program relies upon interaction between the programmer and computer.

T   F   2. An advantage of the stand-alone program is its easy repeatability for production runs.

T   F   3. Stand-alone programs are usually written to solve a particular problem.

T   F   4. Stand-alone programs usually require considerable programming time on the part of the user each time they are run.

T   F   5. Stand-alone programs are best suited to one-time, nonrepetitive problems.

T   F   6. The following steps are in sequence: problem analysis, coding, algorithm, keypunching.

T   F   7. The following steps are in sequence: keypunch, run, debug, document.

T   F   8. Coding involves converting a keypunched deck into a set of written instructions.

T   F   9. Each compiler translates a single language.

T   F   10. During the algorithm and flowcharting phase, the programmer studies the problem and defines the steps to solve it.

T   F   11. Bugs are errors in program logic.

T   F   12. Each line on the coding form is converted into a single punched card.

T   F   13. Before a job may be run, it is assembled with job control cards.

T   F   14. Only statements without bugs are compiled, ready for execution.

T   F   15. The process of inserting job control cards into the job stream is called de-bugging.

T   F   16. The graphic narration is a list of program bugs.

T   F   17. A program may compile properly but not give correct results.

T   F   18. An abstract is often found in the documentation file.

T   F   19. The two common types of bugs in a program are computation errors and execution errors.

T   F   20. The documentation step usually comes before the keypunching phase.

MATCHING STATEMENTS Select the matching description for each term from the list on the right.

_____	1. Problem analysis	a. Graphic illustration
_____	2. Flowcharting	b. Removing error
_____	3. Coding form	c. Short summary
_____	4. Debugging	d. Record during run
_____	5. Error in spelling	e. Study problem
_____	6. Number too large for storage	f. Compilation error
_____	7. Abstract	g. Master list for checking
_____	8. Run manual	h. Execution error
_____	9. Program listing	i. Errors flagged by compiler
_____	10. Diagnostic message	j. Ruled off in columns

MULTIPLE CHOICE STATEMENTS Circle the correct answer or answers for each statement.

1. One of the following is *not* a characteristic of the stand-alone program.
   a. suited to one time problem
   b. useful for repetitive production run
   c. written for a specific problem
   d. can run on several data sets

2. Nonrecurring, nonrepetitive problems are best solved
   a. without a computer
   b. in the interactive mode
   c. both A and B
   d. none of the above

3. The function of coding is to
   a. diagnose problems and solve them
   b. plan algorithms
   c. write set of instructions
   d. none of the above

4. Programming instructions must conform to
   a. rules of spelling
   b. rules of structure
   c. rules of syntax
   d. all of the above

5. The function of coding forms is to
   a. document output
   b. provide page on which to write computer instructions
   c. write descriptive narrative
   d. draw graphic narration

6. During keypunching, the operator converts

    a. handwritten instructions into machine language
    b. machine language into machine-readable form
    c. handwritten instructions into machine-readable form
    d. none of the above

7. At present, the major means of inputting data into the computer for stand-alone programs is

    a. cards
    b. magnetic tape
    c. magnetic disk
    d. none of the above

8. The assembled deck, including job control cards, is called

    a. job stream
    b. job sequence
    c. coding stream
    d. none of the above

9. The most common cause of programming failure is

    a. bugs in hardware
    b. bugs in program
    c. bugs in documentation
    d. none of the above

10. One of the following is *not* a method of flagging or marking errors.

    a. listing at beginning of program
    b. dollar sign at point of error
    c. carat sign at point of error
    d. listing at bottom of program

SHORT ESSAY QUESTIONS

1. Describe the stand-alone program and how it is used.

2. Describe how coding forms are used in writing a program.

3. Summarize the purpose of running and debugging a program.

4. Describe the purpose of diagnostic messages.

5. Describe the contents of a documentation file.

6. Summarize the major steps in developing the stand-alone program.

7. Summarize the advantages and limitations of the stand-alone program.

ANSWERS TO SELF-TESTS

1. F	11. T	1. e	1. a
2. T	12. T	2. a	2. c
3. T	13. T	3. j	3. c
4. F	14. T	4. b	4. d
5. F	15. F	5. f	5. b
6. F	16. F	6. h	6. c
7. T	17. T	7. c	7. a
8. F	18. T	8. d	8. a
9. T	19. F	9. g	9. b
10. T	20. F	10. i	10. a

Supplied and
Interactive Programs

VOCABULARY Briefly define the following terms.

1. Supplied program

2. Manufacturer-supplied program

3. Proprietary program

4. Interactive program

5. Time-sharing company

6. Interactive terminal

7. Conversational programming

8. Real time

9. On line

10. User-supplied program

SELF-TESTS

TRUE AND FALSE STATEMENTS

T   F   1.   Supplied programs are always written by the user.

T   F   2.   Supplied programs are by nature easily used by others.

T   F   3.   Supplied programs are sometimes called ready-made programs.

T   F   4.   Computer manufacturers often develop programs for use by customers.

T   F   5.   Finance, personnel, and inventory programs are examples of manufacturer-supplied programs.

T   F   6.   Business firms rarely make their programs available to other users.

T   F   7.   Only public schools and universities are proprietary suppliers.

T   F   8.   Proprietary firms specialize in developing and writing programs, but do not market them.

T   F   9.   Proprietary programs generally have widespread applications.

T   F   10.   Proprietary programs may be made available for a flat fee or monthly rental or lease charge.

T   F   11.   File maintenance and data plotting are examples of proprietary programs.

T   F   12.   Few proprietary software firms make abstracts of their programs available.

T   F   13.   Programs provided by vendors are often delivered as cards, reels of tape, or disks.

T   F   14.   Few firms find ready-made programs from computer manufacturers economical.

T   F   15.   Supplied programs often take many months to deliver and, hence, slow down the data processing effort.

T   F   16.   Some suppliers provide maintenance, revision, and modification services as part of the rental agreement.

T   F   17.   There has been an increase in the number of firms providing proprietary software.

T   F   18.   File maintenance programs are available from proprietary software firms.

T   F   19.   Time-sharing companies do not offer interactive programming services.

T   F   20.   Interactive programs have few or no branches or options.

MATCHING STATEMENTS Select the matching description for each term from the list on the right.

_____	1.	Supplied program	a.	Programs for profit
_____	2.	Interactive program	b.	Meets specific needs
_____	3.	Self-documenting	c.	Connected directly to computer
_____	4.	Program selection	d.	Ready-made program
_____	5.	On-line	e.	Terminal print out
_____	6.	Real-time	f.	Programs for customers
_____	7.	Time-sharing company	g.	Process query instantaneously
_____	8.	Proprietary software supplier	h.	Review library
_____	9.	Manufacturer-supplied program	i.	Conversational in nature
_____	10.	User-supplied program	j.	Sell computer time

MULTIPLE CHOICE STATEMENTS Circle the correct answer or answers for each statement.

1. Which of the following are characteristics of the supplied program?

   a. written by user
   b. provided by computer manufacturer
   c. available for flat fee
   d. available on monthly lease

2. Manufacturer-supplied programs are characterized by

   a. provided at little or no cost
   b. generalized in nature
   c. available from manufacturer
   d. all of the above

3. The advantage of interactive programming is

   a. instantaneous results
   b. lower cost
   c. higher volume
   d. all of the above

4. User-supplied programs are characterized by

   a. availability to manufacturer for distribution
   b. distribution without charge
   c. ability to handle many business applications
   d. all of the above

5. Interactive programming requires

   a. little or no programming skill
   b. advanced hardware knowledge
   c. advanced mathematical skill
   d. all of the above

6. File maintenance routines may include such things as
   a. searches
   b. merges
   c. removal of inactive records
   d. all of the above

7. Commercial banking packages handle which of the following?
   a. process mortgage payments and certificates of deposit
   b. plan advertising
   c. recruit personnel
   d. provide management reports

8. Which of the following are characteristics of the supplied program?
   a. saves programming effort
   b. saves programming time
   c. is untested
   d. contains extra services

9. One of the following is *not* a characteristic of interactive programming.
   a. data processed instantaneously
   b. data brought to computer center
   c. programs available and documented on-line
   d. practical for one-time only problems

10. Supplied programs are written by
    a. the user
    b. someone other than user
    c. private or public institutions
    d. proprietary software houses

SHORT ESSAY QUESTIONS

1. Summarize the characteristics of the supplied program.

2. Discuss proprietary software suppliers. Mention the services they offer.

3. How does the interactive program differ from the stand-alone program?

4. What are some of the supplied programs available to users?

5. Discuss the interactive terminal and its functions.

ANSWERS TO SELF-TESTS

1. F	11. T	1. d	1. b,c,d
2. T	12. F	2. i	2. d
3. T	13. T	3. e	3. a
4. T	14. F	4. h	4. d
5. T	15. F	5. c	5. a
6. F	16. T	6. g	6. d
7. F	17. T	7. j	7. a,d
8. F	18. T	8. a	8. a,b,d
9. T	19. F	9. f	9. b
10. T	20. F	10. b	10. b,c,d

Operating Systems

VOCABULARY Briefly define the following terms.

1. Operating system

2. Control programs

3. Service programs

4. Resident storage device

5. Processing programs

6. Job control program

7. Language translator

8. Job stream

9. System library

10. Input/output control program

SELF-TESTS

TRUE AND FALSE STATEMENTS

T F   1. Computers cannot diagnose their own problems, nor detect errors within the system.

T F   2. Operating systems are relatively simple programs supplied by the computer user.

T F   3. Operating systems increase throughput by scheduling work in the most efficient way.

T F   4. Operating systems are composed of the following two major programs: control programs, selective programs.

T F   5. Control programs log jobs, monitor system status, and communicate with operator.

T F   6. Service programs include language translators and maintain the system library.

T F   7. Tape operating systems store the operating system on disk resident devices.

T F   8. Interruptions are handled by the service program.

T F   9. Control programs oversee the overall operation of the system and reduce idle operating time.

T F   10. The supervisor program pulls routines from storage and loads them into core.

T F   11. The job control program schedules input/output operations.

T F   12. Small computers may have only one or two language translators.

T F   13. Sort/merge programs maintain the system library.

T F   14. The transfer of data from card to tape, from tape to a line printer, or from disk to tape is handled by utility programs.

T F   15. The first thing the operating system does is log in the name of the job and the time.

T F   16. An object deck is a set of instructions in machine language stored on a secondary storage device.

T F   17. The job control program recognizes special symbols such as question marks, dollar signs, or slashes.

T F   18. The job card always follows the compiler card.

T F   19. The compiler card always comes ahead of the execute card.

T F   20. The end-of-job (EOJ) card is always the last card in the job stream.

MATCHING STATEMENTS Select the matching description for each term from the list on the right.

_____ 1. Service program
_____ 2. Control program
_____ 3. Job control cards
_____ 4. Resident storage device
_____ 5. DOS
_____ 6. TOS
_____ 7. System library
_____ 8. Supervisor program
_____ 9. IOCS
_____ 10. Language translator

a. Stores routines
b. Disk resident system
c. Inserted into job stream
d. Handles scheduling
e. Compiler
f. Loads language translator
g. Handles interruptions
h. Input/output control system
i. Tape resident system
j. Holds operating system

MULTIPLE CHOICE STATEMENTS Circle the correct answer or answers for each statement.

1. Which of the following are names for the operating system?
   a. master control program
   b. planetary supervisor
   c. executive control system
   d. comprehensive operating supervisor

2. Which of the following are functions of control programs?
   a. combine job phases
   b. monitor phases
   c. log jobs
   d. maintain system library

3. One of the following is _not_ a common operating system.
   a. GOS
   b. TOS
   c. DOS
   d. BOS

4. The function of the language translator is to
   a. translate FORTRAN to COBOL
   b. translate FORTRAN to machine language
   c. translate machine language to FORTRAN
   d. all of the above

5. The job stream consists of
   a. file of language translators
   b. jobs and job control cards
   c. job control cards
   d. none of the above

6. Utility programs perform the following functions:
   a. reblock data
   b. transfer data from card to tape
   c. transfer data from tape to card
   d. all of the above

7. Which of the following are common job control cards?
   a. end of job (EOJ)
   b. job card
   c. time card
   d. compiler card

8. Which of the following are common options?
   a. dump compiler
   b. dump main storage
   c. log
   d. list source program

9. The data deck always
   a. comes before the execute card
   b. comes after the execute card
   c. comes after the end-of-job card
   d. none of the above

10. Some systems mark the end of a data deck with
    a. /& END OF JOB
    b. /* END OF FILE
    c. /— END OF COMPILER
    d. /% END OF OPTION

SHORT ESSAY QUESTIONS

1. Summarize the advantages of operating systems.

2. Summarize the function of control programs.

3. Discuss the function of language translators.

4. Discuss service programs. Include types and purpose.

5. Describe the four major job control cards and their functions.

6. Discuss how utility programs are used.

7. What is the function of the input/output control program?

ANSWERS TO SELF-TESTS

1.	F	11.	F	1.	f	1.	a,c,d
2.	F	12.	T	2.	g	2.	a,b,c
3.	T	13.	F	3.	c	3.	a
4.	F	14.	T	4.	j	4.	b
5.	T	15.	T	5.	b	5.	b
6.	T	16.	F	6.	i	6.	d
7.	F	17.	T	7.	a	7.	a,b,d
8.	F	18.	F	8.	d	8.	b,c,d
9.	T	19.	T	9.	h	9.	b
10.	T	20.	T	10.	e	10.	b

COBOL Programming Language

VOCABULARY Briefly define the following terms.

1. Standard character set

2. Reserved word

3. Names

4. Optional words

5. File section

6. Identification Division

7. Environment Division

8. Data Division

9. Procedure Division

10. Problem-oriented language

SELF-TESTS

TRUE AND FALSE STATEMENTS

T F 1. COBOL is an example of a POL.

T F 2. COBOL is unique in that it is primarily supported by computer manufacturers.

T F 3. COBOL is regularly evaluated, altered, and improved through a user's committee.

T F 4. COBOL was designed specially to reflect common business usage.

T F 5. COBOL closely resembles mathematical notation and algebraic equations.

T F 6. COBOL is able to manipulate words, sentences, and paragraphs of textual matter.

T F 7. COBOL is machine independent, a characteristic that allows it to be run on different makes and models of computers with little revision.

T F 8. COBOL is a tightly written language with few mathematical limitations.

T F 9. The standard character set is the approved list of reserved words that may be used in the program.

T F 10. Because of COBOL's free form, it has few rules of sentence structure, spelling, or syntax.

T F 11. Reserved words are assigned by the programmer to represent quantities.

T F 12. Names are assigned by the programmer to represent data calculated or stored in the computer.

T F 13. Optional words affect the program flow.

T F 14. The standard COBOL coding form has 80 columns and 25 lines for instructions.

T F 15. In COBOL, columns 8 to 72 are reserved for programming statements, and column 7 is reserved as a continuation column.

T F 16. The second major division in COBOL is the Data Division.

T F 17. The Identification Division specifies the input/output devices to be assigned to the program.

T F 18. The Data Division tells the computer the kind and format of data being read in.

T F 19. The Procedure Division directs the program to open files, move data, perform calculations.

T F 20. The READ data statements cause the computer to branch after making a logical decision.

MATCHING STATEMENTS Select the matching description for each term from the list on the right.

_____ 1. CODASYL
_____ 2. Data Division
_____ 3. Literal capability
_____ 4. Machine independent
_____ 5. Standard character set
_____ 6. Reserved words
_____ 7. Names
_____ 8. Optional words
_____ 9. Columns 8 to 72
_____ 10. Procedure Division

a. Approved list of symbols
b. Statements
c. Assigned by programmer
d. No effect on program
e. Define steps
f. Describes record format
g. User group
h. Run on several machines
i. Manipulate text matter
j. Assigned by compiler

MULTIPLE CHOICE STATEMENTS Circle the correct answer or answers for each statement.

1. POL stands for
   a. programming-operator language
   b. process-oriented language
   c. procedure-operating limit
   d. none of the above

2. The WRITE statement instructs the computer to
   a. perform calculations
   b. input data
   c. output data
   d. none of the above

3. COBOL is supported primarily by
   a. manufacturer's group
   b. user's group
   c. manufacturers and proprietary firms
   d. none of the above

4. A characteristic of COBOL is
   a. good literal capability
   b. excellent mathematical capability
   c. close resemblance to mathematical notation
   d. none of the above

5. One of the following is *not* a characteristic of COBOL.
   a. wordy and verbose
   b. machine independent
   c. requires large amount of core
   d. has few rules and conventions

6. COBOL standard character set consists of
   a. a limited list of characters
   b. a limited list of words
   c. a limited list of sentences
   d. all of the above

7. In COBOL, sentences are grouped to form
   a. blocks
   b. paragraphs
   c. pages
   d. formulas

8. In COBOL, most statements terminate with a
   a. colon
   b. period
   c. semicolon
   d. hyphen

9. The PERFORM statement
   a. instructs the computer to loop
   b. includes the word PERFORM
   c. may have a pre-set limit
   d. all of the above

10. The branching statement causes the computer to
    a. test a quantity and stop
    b. make a logical decision
    c. test a quantity and branch
    d. branch and test a quantity

SHORT ESSAY QUESTIONS

1. Describe the general characteristics of the COBOL language.

2. What is the function of the Data Division?

3. Summarize the advantages and limitations of COBOL.

4. What is the function of the Procedure Division?

5. Discuss the general form of the WRITE data statement.

6. Summarize the functions of reserved words in COBOL.

7. How are names used in COBOL?

ANSWERS TO SELF-TESTS

1. T	11. F	1. g	1. d
2. F	12. T	2. f	2. c
3. T	13. F	3. i	3. b
4. T	14. T	4. h	4. a
5. F	15. T	5. a	5. d
6. T	16. F	6. j	6. a
7. T	17. F	7. c	7. b
8. F	18. T	8. d	8. b
9. F	19. T	9. b	9. d
10. F	20. F	10. e	10. c

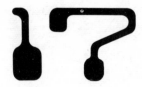

FORTRAN Programming Language

VOCABULARY Briefly define the following terms.

1. Control statement

2. Arithmetic statement

3. Input/output statement

4. FORMAT statement

5. Constant

6. Variable

7. Integer

8. Real number

9. Literal constant

10. Array

SELF-TESTS

TRUE AND FALSE STATEMENTS

T   F   1. FORTRAN is short for the words FORmula TRANsmission.

T   F   2. FORTRAN was originally conceived of as a language for scientists and mathematicians.

T   F   3. Each computer manufacturer or user modifies FORTRAN to suit his own needs.

T   F   4. FORTRAN has excellent mathematical and numeric capabilities.

T   F   5. FORTRAN closely resembles algebraic equations.

T   F   6. Since FORTRAN tends to be wordy and verbose, each program requires many statements.

T   F   7. FORTRAN compilers are available on both large and small computers.

T   F   8. FORTRAN requires more documentation than COBOL to explain the logic in the program.

T   F   9. A control statement directs the computer to read in or write out data.

T   F   10. Subtraction, exponentiation, and square root are carried out by arithmetic statements.

T   F   11. FORMAT statements indicate whether data will be whole or decimal numbers.

T   F   12. A variable is a string of characters considered as a single group.

T   F   13. The number 113.28 is an example of a real number.

T   F   14. The value T509 is an integer.

T   F   15. A subscript indicates the position of a storage location within an array.

T   F   16. A function is a mathematical subprogram that can be called in by a problem program.

T   F   17. SQRT is an example of a built-in subroutine.

T   F   18. Subroutines are always written by the computer manufacturer.

T   F   19. A subroutine is referenced by its name.

T   F   20. The LIST COMMENT statement directs the computer to perform a mathematical calculation.

MATCHING STATEMENTS Select the matching description for each term from the list on the right.

_____	1. Function	a. Called in by program
_____	2. Subroutine	b. Whole number
_____	3. Array	c. Mathematical subprogram
_____	4. Integer	d. Governs sequence of operation
_____	5. Literal constant	e. Describes information
_____	6. Variable	f. Related storage locations
_____	7. Constant	g. Changes during run
_____	8. FORMAT statement	h. Controls flow in and out of CPU
_____	9. Input/output statement	i. String of characters
_____	10. Control statement	j. Fixed quantity

MULTIPLE CHOICE STATEMENTS Circle the correct answer or answers for each statement.

1. FORTRAN stands for
   a. FORmat TRANsmission
   b. FORmulation Program
   c. FORth TRANsistor
   d. FORmula TRANslating System

2. FORTRAN was originally designed for
   a. teachers and educators
   b. businessmen and accountants
   c. scientists and mathematicians
   d. salesmen and executives

3. Which of the following are characteristics of FORTRAN?
   a. excellent mathematical capability
   b. excellent ability to manipulate textual material
   c. very compact language
   d. eliminates routine housekeeping details

4. Which of the following are types of FORTRAN statements?
   a. PERFORM statement
   b. arithmetic statement
   c. FORMAT statement
   d. control statement

5. Which of the following are functions of the FORMAT statement?
   a. describe kind of data to be input
   b. describe speed of input
   c. describe fields where data is located
   d. describe number of digits in data

6. Which of the following columns are *not* read by the compiler?

   a. columns 1–5
   b. column 6
   c. columns 7–72
   d. columns 73–80

7. Which of the following are integers?

   a. 100.0
   b. 1,000
   c. 9,903
   d. 2

8. Which of the following are common FORTRAN statements?

   a. READ
   b. WRITE
   c. STUDY
   d. DO

9. One of the following is an improperly structured mathematical statement.

   a. A = B + C
   b. A = B
   c. A + B = C
   d. EFFECT = 10 + ENERGY

10. Which of the following are characteristics of the DO statement?

   a. repeats a sequence
   b. extends to a CONTINUE statement
   c. contains an index
   d. bypasses a sequence

SHORT ESSAY QUESTIONS

1. Contrast the capabilities of FORTRAN with those of COBOL.

2. What are the differences between a constant and a variable?

3. Discuss how FORTRAN was developed and is maintained.

4. What are the functions of arrays and how are they used in FORTRAN?

5. Describe how subroutines are used.

6. Discuss the types of problems that can best be solved using the FORTRAN language.

7. Summarize the functions of FORMAT statements.

ANSWERS TO SELF-TESTS

1.	F	11.	T	1.	c	1.	d
2.	T	12.	F	2.	a	2.	c
3.	T	13.	T	3.	f	3.	a,c,d
4.	T	14.	F	4.	b	4.	b,c,d
5.	T	15.	T	5.	i	5.	a,c,d
6.	F	16.	T	6.	g	6.	d
7.	T	17.	F	7.	j	7.	b,c,d
8.	T	18.	F	8.	e	8.	a,b,d
9.	F	19.	T	9.	h	9.	c
10.	T	20.	F	10.	d	10.	a,b,c

Other Programming
Languages Used in Business

VOCABULARY   Briefly define the following terms.

1.   Programming Language I

2.   Default option

3.   Report Program Generator

4.   Assembler language

5.   A Programming Language

6.   Beginners All-Purpose Symbolic Instruction Code

7.   Administrative Terminal System

8.   Text stream

9. Operator

10. Identifier

SELF-TESTS

TRUE AND FALSE STATEMENTS

T   F   1. Only about 12 computer languages have been written and are in use today.

T   F   2. Most early computer languages were developed for interactive processing applications.

T   F   3. Interactive languages are best suited to real-time remote processing.

T   F   4. Languages may be classified as either interactive or batch.

T   F   5. RPG is a batch processing language.

T   F   6. APL and ATS are interactive languages.

T   F   7. PL/I is suitable only for batch processing.

T   F   8. An advantage of PL/I is its free style and lack of restrictions regarding columns.

T   F   9. PL/I requires a sizable amount of primary storage and cannot be run on small computers.

T   F   10. PL/I uses about 50 powerful operators.

T   F   11. RPG is a standardized language.

T   F   12. Assembler language is machine dependent.

T   F   13. Assembler language programs are more efficient than PL/I programs on the computer.

T   F   14. Assembler language uses harmonic codes that assign names and storage locations.

T   F   15. Operations are initiated by machine language codes in Assembler language.

T   F   16. Most Assembler instructions have four parts.

T   F   17. A standard form is used to code Assembler language instructions.

T   F   18. APL has two modes: definition and execution.

T   F   19. APL can be run on small computers because it requires little primary storage.

T   F   20. ATS is an interactive language designed primarily for processing algebraic and mathematical problems.

MATCHING STATEMENTS Select the matching description for each term from the list on the right.

_____	1.	PL/I
_____	2.	RPG
_____	3.	Assembler language
_____	4.	APL
_____	5.	ATS
_____	6.	BASIC
_____	7.	Text stream
_____	8.	Editing
_____	9.	Line-by-line execution
_____	10.	Registers

a. Assembler programming
b. Default options
c. Powerful operators
d. Revisions or changes
e. Prepare reports
f. Mnemonic code
g. Input characters
h. Text editing
i. Execution mode
j. Simple I/O commands

MULTIPLE CHOICE STATEMENTS Circle the correct answer or answers for each statement.

1. Which of the following are batch processing languages?
    a. RPG
    b. APL
    c. COBOL
    d. FORTRAN

2. Which of the following are interactive languages?
    a. BASIC
    b. APL
    c. ATS
    d. QSL

3. Advantages of PL/I include
    a. requires large compiler
    b. default options
    c. limited to IBM machine
    d. none of the above

4. Which are characteristics of PL/I?
    a. rigid coding conventions
    b. data entered as stream of characters
    c. identifiers
    d. free form language

5. Which are major tasks in RPG?
    a. file segregation
    b. file description
    c. file maintenance
    d. outputting results

6. Which of the following are common RPG specification forms?
    a. input specifications
    b. retrieval specifications
    c. calculation specifications
    d. output format specifications

7. In Assembler, statements are translated into machine language
    a. line for line
    b. each instruction generates many lines
    c. many instructions generate one line
    d. none of the above

8. An advantage of Assembler language is
    a. programs are fast and easy to write
    b. programs are machine dependent
    c. programs fully utilize primary storage
    d. all of the above

9. Which of the following are characteristics of APL?
    a. execution mode
    b. powerful operators
    c. definition mode
    d. default options

10. Which are characteristics of BASIC?
    a. uses Teletype terminals
    b. allows paper tape I/O
    c. has powerful operators
    d. does not require detailed format descriptions

SHORT ESSAY QUESTIONS

1. Describe the differences between batch processing and interactive languages.

2. How do the programming conventions of PL/I differ from those of FORTRAN?

3. How is text editing performed using ATS?

4. Summarize how programs are entered and processed using BASIC language.

5. What is the difference between the execution and definition modes in APL?

6. Summarize the advantages of BASIC.

7. Summarize the advantages of APL.

ANSWERS TO SELF-TESTS

1. F	11. F	1. b	1. a,c,d
2. F	12. T	2. e	2. a,b,c
3. T	13. T	3. f	3. b
4. T	14. F	4. c	4. b,c,d
5. T	15. T	5. h	5. b,c,d
6. T	16. F	6. j	6. a,c,d
7. F	17. T	7. g	7. a
8. T	18. T	8. d	8. c
9. T	19. F	9. i	9. a,b,c
10. F	20. F	10. a	10. a,b,d

Introduction to Business Systems

VOCABULARY Briefly define the following terms.

1. Business system

2. Business systems analyst

3. Simulation

4. Model

5. Linear Programming

6. PERT

7. System implementation

8. Brush-fire approach

9. Scientific method

10. Job order

SELF-TESTS

TRUE AND FALSE STATEMENTS

T   F   1. Business systems include software and hardware, but not policy and methods.

T   F   2. Subsystems are smaller units of a system and must act in accord with the larger system.

T   F   3. The board of directors carries out the decisions of management.

T   F   4. The board of directors sets objectives and management carries them out.

T   F   5. Business data is of use primarily to the board of directors and of little value to management.

T   F   6. To be of value, business data must be gathered, processed, and reported at a reasonable cost.

T   F   7. The brush-fire approach to problem solving is sometimes known as the scientific method.

T   F   8. The hunch and chance play important roles in scientific systems analysis.

T   F   9. The first step in the scientific method is system planning and analysis.

T   F   10. Feedback is not an essential element in evaluation.

T   F   11. Business models involve constructing physical devices that are miniatures of actual installations.

T   F   12. The PERT technique is used in developing aerospace, shipbuilding, and construction projects.

T   F   13. The business systems department is not responsible for system implementation.

T   F   14. The business systems department is responsible for forms design and office layout.

T   F   15. Personnel selection, including job descriptions, is usually beyond the scope of the systems department.

T   F   16. Hardware selection, including evaluating computer cost and capabilities, is within the domain of the systems department.

T   F   17. The business systems department draws from only the data processing and statistics fields.

T   F   18. Finding the best mix involves testing all possible combinations to find the one that best solves the problem.

T   F   19. Simulations and models reduce the chances of making costly errors in real situations.

T   F   20.   Since a model is run on the computer, there is little need to test it with known data.

MATCHING STATEMENTS Select the matching description for each term from the list on the right.

_____	1. Decision making	a. Installing new system
_____	2. Business system	b. Early problem-solving technique
_____	3. Subsystem	c. First step
_____	4. System implementation	d. Need for complete, relevant data
_____	5. System design	e. Single element
_____	6. Brush-fire problem solving	f. Last step
_____	7. Systems analysis	g. John Dewey
_____	8. Scientific method	h. Sum of the parts
_____	9. Recognize and diagnose problem	i. Planning new system
_____	10. Evaluation	j. Modern problem-solving technique

MULTIPLE CHOICE STATEMENTS Circle the correct answer or answers for each statement.

1. Which are characteristics of a business system?
   a. collection of procedures and techniques
   b. has several divergent goals
   c. composed of subsystems
   d. involves people and machines

2. One of the following is *not* an early problem-solving technique.
   a. the guess
   b. intuition
   c. scientific method
   d. rule of thumb

3. To be most valuable to a firm, data should
   a. be available at the right time and place
   b. be of suitable accuracy
   c. be of the right kind and quality
   d. all of the above

4. The purpose of defining the problem is to
   a. state the problem in a quantitative way
   b. state the problem in a qualitative way
   c. evaluate the problem
   d. implement the solution

5. Which of the following are computerized problem-solving techniques?
   a. PERT
   b. LP
   c. modeling
   d. ALERT

6. Which are responsibilities of the business systems department?

   a. hardware selection
   b. office layout
   c. software preparation
   d. hardware maintenance

7. Which are characteristics of forms design, production, and administration?

   a. plan new forms
   b. consider form size, paper, and type
   c. finance forms
   d. order forms

8. Work measurement involves

   a. time studies, goal studies
   b. goal studies, work sampling studies
   c. goal studies, objective studies
   d. time studies, work sampling studies

9. Which are tasks of the systems analyst?

   a. write job descriptions
   b. outline duties
   c. write job orders
   d. manage retirement fund

10. Which are characteristics of the scientific method?

    a. definition of problem
    b. statistical methods
    c. refusal to consider alternatives
    d. feedback

SHORT ESSAY QUESTIONS

1. Describe the characteristics of a business system.

2. Discuss the functions of procedures and policies.

3. Contrast early methods of solving business problems with present methods.

4. How are simulations and models used?

5. What kinds of questions does the business systems analyst consider?

6. Summarize the steps in the scientific method of problem solving.

7. Discuss the importance of business data in relation to time, cost, and accuracy.

ANSWERS TO SELF-TESTS

1. F	11. F	1. d	1. a,c,d
2. T	12. T	2. h	2. c
3. F	13. F	3. e	3. d
4. T	14. T	4. a	4. a
5. F	15. F	5. i	5. a,b,c
6. T	16. T	6. b	6. a,b,c
7. F	17. F	7. j	7. a,b,d
8. F	18. T	8. g	8. d
9. F	19. T	9. c	9. a,b,c
10. F	20. F	10. f	10. a,b,d

Business Systems Evaluation and Performance

VOCABULARY Briefly define the following terms.

1. Feasibility study

2. Preliminary study

3. Investigative study

4. Final report and recommendations

5. On-going committee

6. Project director

7. Vendors

8. Conversion costs

9. File-oriented firm

10. Calculation-oriented firm

SELF-TESTS

TRUE AND FALSE STATEMENTS

T F 1. Most business decisions are easily recalled.

T F 2. Implementation costs may involve altering the physical plant, for example, by installing air conditioning and special floors.

T F 3. Labor costs are rarely considered when evaluating a new system.

T F 4. Many non-monetary benefits, such as human factors and intangible benefits, are evaluated in a new system.

T F 5. The first phase of a feasibility study is an investigative study.

T F 6. The preliminary study answers the question, "Is further study warranted?"

T F 7. An on-going committee is charged with a one-time responsibility of evaluating a new proposal.

T F 8. The task force is a committee formed from employees of several departments.

T F 9. Secondary storage capability is relatively unimportant.

T F 10. One-time costs are usually not considered in evaluating a new system.

T F 11. The final report reports the results of the entire study.

T F 12. Final reports summarize benefits of the new system and conversion costs, but do not include a list of equipment necessary.

T F 13. Manual data processing methods are usually too expensive for small volumes of data.

T F 14. In selecting hardware, both vendor and equipment capability are judged.

T F 15. Vendor capability assesses the ability of equipment to perform as promised.

T F 16. In CPU performance evaluation, the number of cards read per minute is considered.

T F 17. Both arithmetic capacity and primary storage capacity are prime elements in evaluating CPU performance.

T F 18. In judging secondary storage performance, the number of disk drives on the system and speed of card readers are evaluated.

T F 19. A program may be tested on several computers to compare time and cost benefits.

T F 20. Overall system performance considers such factors as multiprocessing and remote processing capabilities.

MATCHING STATEMENTS Select the matching description for each term from the list on the right.

_____	1. File oriented	a.	Complex arithmetic
_____	2. Calculation oriented	b.	Medium volume
_____	3. Manual data processing	c.	Evaluate reputation and staff
_____	4. Unit record processing	d.	Density of media
_____	5. Electronic data processing	e.	Large files
_____	6. Vendor capability	f.	Small volume
_____	7. Equipment capability	g.	Evaluate hardware performance
_____	8. CPU performance	h.	Considers word size
_____	9. I/O performance	i.	Large volume
_____	10. Secondary storage performance	j.	Considers lines printed per minute

MULTIPLE CHOICE STATEMENTS Circle the correct answer or answers for each statement.

1. Which of the following elements are measured in comparing systems?
   a. labor costs
   b. advertising costs
   c. maintenance costs
   d. training costs

2. Which of the following are phases of the feasibility study?
   a. preliminary study
   b. supplementary study
   c. investigative study
   d. final report

3. Which are methods of carrying on a feasibility study?
   a. task force
   b. on-going committee
   c. project terminator
   d. project director

4. The factors considered in the investigative study include
   a. cost
   b. software
   c. hardware
   d. all of the above

5. Which elements are questioned by the systems analyst when considering the time factor?
   a. how long to maintain old system
   b. how long consultants should be employed
   c. annual retirement program
   d. business cycles

6. The final report covers
   a. detailed list of equipment needed
   b. conversion costs
   c. benefits
   d. all of the above

7. Which elements are considered when judging vendor capability?
   a. vendor's reputation
   b. vendor's past performance
   c. CPU storage capacity
   d. system's staff

8. Vendor equipment support means that
   a. the vendor will do all programming
   b. the vendor will do no programming
   c. the vendor will repair and service equipment
   d. none of the above

9. I/O performance evaluates
   a. speed of the CPU
   b. secondary storage capacity
   c. CPU cycle time
   d. none of the above

10. Secondary storage performance evaluates
    a. size of characters on screen
    b. arithmetic capability of CPU
    c. density of media
    d. primary storage capacity

SHORT ESSAY QUESTIONS

1. Explain the need for careful measurement of system performance.

2. Discuss the elements measured in system evaluation.

3. What is the function of the preliminary study?

4. What considerations regarding personnel are made when evaluating a new system?

5. What is the function of the investigative study?

6. What is the function of the final report and recommendations?

7. Discuss the elements considered in making hardware selection.

ANSWERS TO SELF-TESTS

1.	F	11.	T	1.	e	1.	a,c,d
2.	T	12.	F	2.	a	2.	a,c,d
3.	F	13.	F	3.	f	3.	a,b,d
4.	T	14.	T	4.	b	4.	d
5.	F	15.	F	5.	i	5.	a,b,d
6.	T	16.	F	6.	c	6.	d
7.	F	17.	T	7.	g	7.	a,b,d
8.	T	18.	F	8.	h	8.	c
9.	F	19.	T	9.	j	9.	d
10.	F	20.	T	10.	d	10.	c

The Data Processing Department

VOCABULARY Briefly define the following terms.

1. Systems analyst

2. Business systems analyst

3. Programmer

4. Operator

5. Centralized data processing

6. Decentralized data processing

7. Systems programmer

8. Cost control

9. Back-up file

10. Turnaround time

SELF-TESTS

TRUE AND FALSE STATEMENTS

T   F   1. The data processing department may be considered a service unit that provides facilities for other units.

T   F   2. There is very little diversity in the size of data processing departments.

T   F   3. EAM operators are generally assigned to programming activities.

T   F   4. Business system analysts are responsible for maintaining the computer's operating system.

T   F   5. Programmers convert systems analysts' programs and flowcharts into instructions.

T   F   6. On occasion, both coding and systems analysis may be done by the same individual.

T   F   7. Individuals who write programs belong under the operations group.

T   F   8. Individuals who plan and expand the operating system belong under the systems group.

T   F   9. Technicians, librarians, and mathematicians belong under the support group.

T   F   10. Turnaround time is the time it takes to keypunch a job.

T   F   11. Short-run jobs (short compile time) are often given greater priority than long-run jobs.

T   F   12. Many small computers located in many locations is called decentralized data processing.

T   F   13. Retraining programs and seminars for employees are sometimes called in-service training.

T   F   14. A large single computer in a single data center is called decentralized data processing.

T   F   15. Decentralization may present difficulties in standardizing procedures and co-ordinating functions.

T   F   16. Few modern data centers permit hands-on operation of large computers.

T   F   17. The data processing requisition form is used to specify personnel needs.

T   F   18. Scheduling and priority systems are aimed at maximizing throughput and slowing down turnaround time.

T   F   19. The smaller the business the greater the number of programming languages needed.

T   F   20. Back-up files are used to prevent unauthorized use of files.

MATCHING STATEMENTS   Select the matching description for each term from the list on the right.

_____	1. Systems analyst	a. Against calamity
_____	2. Business systems analyst	b. Code instructions
_____	3. Cost control	c. Run computer console
_____	4. Turnaround time	d. Solves organizational data problems
_____	5. Back-up file	e. Single large computer
_____	6. Operators	f. Return of results
_____	7. Programmers	g. Programs operating system
_____	8. Centralized data processing	h. Several computers
_____	9. Decentralized data processing	i. Effective computer use
_____	10. Ultrasonic detection system	j. Security measure

MULTIPLE CHOICE STATEMENTS   Circle the correct answer or answers for each statement.

1. Which are characteristic responses of managers and supervisors to a new data processing system?
    a. fear it will reduce power
    b. view it as a status symbol
    c. accept system without concern
    d. show off system

2. Which of the following are responsibilities of the systems group?
    a. maintenance of hardware
    b. maintenance of systems software
    c. planning and expanding operating system
    d. all of the above

3. Which of the following are responsibilities of the operations group?
    a. operate EAM equipment
    b. write programs
    c. operate computer
    d. all of the above

4. Data centers are subject to
    a. only internal hazards
    b. only external hazards
    c. both internal and external hazards
    d. none of the above

5. Which of the following are goals of cost control?
   a. improve advertising program
   b. gain efficient use of data processing staff
   c. maximize services offered
   d. reduce costs

6. The function of the data processing requisition form is to
   a. authorize overtime
   b. authorize sickleave
   c. authorize data processing services
   d. none of the above

7. Centralized data processing services are characterized by
   a. several small computers
   b. one large computer
   c. several locations
   d. none of the above

8. Decentralized data processing is characterized by
   a. several locations
   b. single large computer
   c. standardized procedures
   d. all of the above

9. Which of the following are forms of in-service training?
   a. pre-employment testing program
   b. retraining program
   c. seminar for employees on new procedures
   d. seminar for employees on new equipment

10. Which of the following are members of the support group?
    a. tape librarians
    b. mathematicians
    c. clerk typists
    d. all of the above

SHORT ESSAY QUESTIONS

1. Contrast the functions of the systems analyst and the business systems analyst.

2. Contrast centralized and decentralized data processing services.

3. Describe the use and function of back-up files.

4. Summarize the goals of cost control.

5. Discuss some common physical plant protection measures.

6. Summarize how a data center's personnel needs are satisfied.

ANSWERS TO SELF-TESTS

1. T	11. T	1. g	1. a,b,d
2. F	12. T	2. d	2. b,c
3. F	13. T	3. i	3. a,c
4. F	14. F	4. f	4. c
5. T	15. T	5. a	5. b,c,d
6. T	16. T	6. c	6. c
7. F	17. F	7. b	7. b
8. T	18. F	8. e	8. a
9. T	19. F	9. h	9. b,c,d
10. F	20. F	10. j	10. d

Introduction to Teleprocessing

VOCABULARY Briefly define the following terms.

1. Teleprocessing

2. Telecommunications

3. Data transmission line

4. Multiprocessing

5. Data entry

6. Data inquiry

7. Half-duplex circuit

8. Wide band line

9. Channel

10. Coupler

SELF-TESTS

TRUE AND FALSE STATEMENTS

T F 1. A teleprocessing system requires some kind of communications link.

T F 2. The communications link is an audio output device.

T F 3. Business firms were the earliest users of teleprocessing.

T F 4. Teleprocessing is limited in the variety of tasks it can handle and, hence, is not widely used.

T F 5. A simple teleprocessing system must have at least one remote I/O device.

T F 6. Data entry involves storage of large amounts of data on secondary storage systems.

T F 7. In the off-line data preparation mode, data is fed directly to the CPU from the I/O device.

T F 8. In shared data input, several remote terminals are connected to the CPU through a single transmission line.

T F 9. Simplex circuits have the greatest data transmission capacity.

T F 10. Up to 18,000 BPS can be transmitted on narrow band lines.

T F 11. Voice grade lines cannot be used to transmit digital data.

T F 12. Acoustic couplers convert signals into audible tones for transmission.

T F 13. In real-time processing, transactions are processed the moment they occur.

T F 14. RJE stands for real-time job entry.

T F 15. Audio response and video display are two common means of data inquiry response.

T F 16. Data inquiry cannot be made through a keyboard terminal.

T F 17. Teleprocessing is subject to fewer failures and problems than local processing.

T F 18. A multiplexer is designed to provide several dozen channels of communication.

T F 19. A channel is a path between a terminal and its CPU.

T F 20. Bits per second is the standard measure of data transmission speed.

MATCHING STATEMENTS   Select the matching description for each term from the list on the right.

_____	1.	Channel	a.	Magnetic disk
_____	2.	Multiprogramming	b.	18,000 BPS
_____	3.	Data inquiry	c.	Data entry
_____	4.	Data storage	d.	CPU-terminal path
_____	5.	Coupler	e.	Simultaneous transmission
_____	6.	Narrow band line	f.	300 BPS
_____	7.	Wide band line	g.	Transmit only
_____	8.	Simplex circuit	h.	Execute several programs
_____	9.	Full-duplex circuit	i.	Audio response
_____	10.	Shared data input	j.	Modem

MULTIPLE CHOICE STATEMENTS   Circle the correct answer or answers for each statement.

1. Which are early applications of teleprocessing?
   a. military applications
   b. airline reservations
   c. educational institutions
   d. none of the above

2. Which are common teleprocessing applications?
   a. local batch processing
   b. hotel reservation processing
   c. auto license verification
   d. order entry processing

3. A complex teleprocessing network consists of
   a. large CPU with one remote terminal
   b. small CPU with many terminals
   c. large CPU with many terminals
   d. several CPU's with many terminals

4. Multiprocessing consists of
   a. two or more input terminals
   b. two or more output terminals
   c. two or more CPU's
   d. two or more couplers

5. Which are elements of the basic teleprocessing system?
   a. data relocation
   b. data entry
   c. data transmission
   d. data storage

6. Which of the following are means of data entry?
   a. shared data input
   b. computer accessed data entry
   c. off-line data preparation
   d. off-line data preparation, on-line entry

7. Which are common data transmission lines?
   a. quadriplex circuit
   b. simplex circuit
   c. half-duplex circuit
   d. full-duplex circuit

8. Data transmission lines are classified by
   a. bits per second
   b. bits per minute
   c. bits per storage
   d. words per minute

9. Wide band lines can transmit more than
   a. 180 BPS
   b. 18,000 BPS
   c. 180,000 BPS
   d. 1,800 BPS

10. Which of the following are names for a coupling device?
    a. interface facility
    b. accumulator-translator
    c. modem
    d. modulator-demodulator

SHORT ESSAY QUESTIONS

1. Discuss a multiplexer device. Include its function.

2. What is the function of acoustic couplers?

3. Discuss channels and their use in data transmission.

4. What are the differences between the three major kinds of data transmission lines?

5. Summarize several modes of data entry.

6. Summarize the advantages and limitations of teleprocessing.

7. Describe the remote job entry system and how it is used.

ANSWERS TO SELF-TESTS

1. T	11. F	1. d	1. a,b
2. F	12. T	2. h	2. b,c,d
3. F	13. T	3. i	3. d
4. F	14. F	4. a	4. c
5. T	15. T	5. j	5. b,c,d
6. F	16. F	6. f	6. a,b,d
7. F	17. F	7. b	7. b,c,d
8. T	18. T	8. g	8. a
9. F	19. T	9. e	9. b
10. F	20. T	10. c	10. a,c,d

The Computer As a Utility

VOCABULARY Briefly define the following terms.

1. Computer utility

2. Service bureau

3. Time-sharing service

4. Data bank services

5. Query terminal

6. Data base

7. Discriptor

8. Back-up resource

9. Information retrieval

10. Production run

SELF-TESTS

TRUE AND FALSE STATEMENTS

T   F   1.   On-line text editing services are used frequently in the preparation of reports, manuals, and bulletins.

T   F   2.   Basic terminal support is used to provide super calculators to remote users.

T   F   3.   An information retrieval system requires extensive storage capacity for data files.

T   F   4.   Most computer utilities do not provide educational services.

T   F   5.   Sales information is often placed in a data bank.

T   F   6.   Data banks are storehouses of generalized information.

T   F   7.   Purchase of utility services relieves the strain on working capital.

T   F   8.   Generally, remote processing adds complexity and increases the chances of equipment failure.

T   F   9.   Firms that lease computing equipment have little opportunity to schedule their own work.

T   F   10. Most computer utilities require customers to sign a contract and establish minimum charges.

T   F   11. Few utilities provide manuals or applications libraries for users.

T   F   12. On-line libraries are an important part of the services offered by utilities.

T   F   13. Most major utilities provide interactive language facilities to users.

T   F   14. Production runs consist of one-time jobs of an experimental nature.

T   F   15. Some firms find it advantageous to buy consulting services from a utility.

T   F   16. In addition to batch processing, some utilities offer pickup and delivery service of documents and cards.

T   F   17. Remote processing requires complex communications equipment.

T   F   18. Programming, testing, and debugging are not provided by utilities.

T   F   19. Most computer utilities require customers to provide keypunched and verified data since they do not offer these services.

T   F   20. Systems engineering and analysis is often an important service offered by utilities.

MATCHING STATEMENTS Select the matching description for each term from the list on the right.

_____	1.	Service bureau	a. On-line terminals
_____	2.	Time sharing service	b. Unit record machines
_____	3.	Data bank service	c. Located at user's establishment
_____	4.	Query terminal	d. Maintain file
_____	5.	Data base	e. Manuals, reports
_____	6.	EAM room	f. Computer utility
_____	7.	Pickup and delivery service	g. BASIC and APL
_____	8.	Interactive languages	h. Central file accessed by user
_____	9.	On-line text editing	i. Discriptor
_____	10.	Production run	j. Utility service

MULTIPLE CHOICE STATEMENTS Circle the correct answer or answers for each statement.

1. Which are characteristics of a computer utility?
   a. offers broad range of services
   b. service for profit
   c. not available to other businesses
   d. provides time sharing services

2. Which are user-site services provided by utilities?
   a. EAM room
   b. time sharing services
   c. data bank services
   d. remote batch processing

3. Which are typical items found in a data base?
   a. financial information
   b. cost of materials
   c. programming personnel
   d. current selling prices

4. A discriptor is a
   a. key word describing selected hardware
   b. key word describing selected personnel
   c. key word describing selected data
   d. none of the above

5. Which of the following are reasons for using a utility?
   a. increase priority and control
   b. increase capacity
   c. provide back-up resource
   d. handle one-time large job

6. Which of the following are services provided at the utility site?
   a. EAM room
   b. programming
   c. program testing and debugging
   d. all of the above

7. The following steps are taken in developing a data base:
   a. define base
   b. structure files
   c. input raw data
   d. all of the above

8. A major portion of the utility's business is
   a. computer design
   b. experimental programming
   c. production runs
   d. none of the above

9. Utilities provide the following interactive languages:
   a. FORTRAN
   b. APL
   c. BASIC
   d. PL/I

10. Offices use the following service(s) to prepare reports and manuals:
    a. on-line libraries
    b. EAM services
    c. on-line text editing
    d. production runs

SHORT ESSAY QUESTIONS

1. Summarize the advantages of using utility services.

2. Summarize the services provided by utilities at their own sites.

3. Describe how data banks are used.

4. Give a brief history of computer utility services.

5. Summarize the services provided at the user's site.

6. Summarize the elements considered in selecting a utility rather than in-house computer service.

ANSWERS TO SELF-TESTS

1.	T	11.	F	1.	f	1.	a,b,d
2.	T	12.	T	2.	a	2.	b,c,d
3.	T	13.	T	3.	h	3.	a,b,d
4.	F	14.	F	4.	c	4.	c
5.	T	15.	T	5.	i	5.	b,c,d
6.	T	16.	T	6.	b	6.	d
7.	T	17.	T	7.	j	7.	d
8.	T	18.	F	8.	g	8.	c
9.	F	19.	F	9.	e	9.	b,c,d
10.	T	20.	T	10.	d	10.	c

B 3
C 4
D 5
E 6
F 7
G 8
H 9
I 0
J 1
  2

Notes